PIPE FITTINGS

NIPPLES

PIPE LENGTHS UP TO 22 FT.

STRAIGHT COUPLING

REDUCING COUPLING

COUPLING

NUT

CAP

STRAIGHT TEE

REDUCING TEE

STREET TEE

STRAIGHT CROSS

REDUCING CROSS

90° ELBOW

90° ELBOW

90° ELBOW

45° ELBOW

REDUCING ELBOW

90° STREET ELBOW

45° STREET ELBOW

45° Y-BEND

REDUCING TEE

REDUCER

UNION (3 PARTS)

PLUG

BUSHING

CAP

RETURN BEND

90°

45°

STREET

UNION ELBOWS

UNION TEES

PLUG

45° ELBOW

TEE

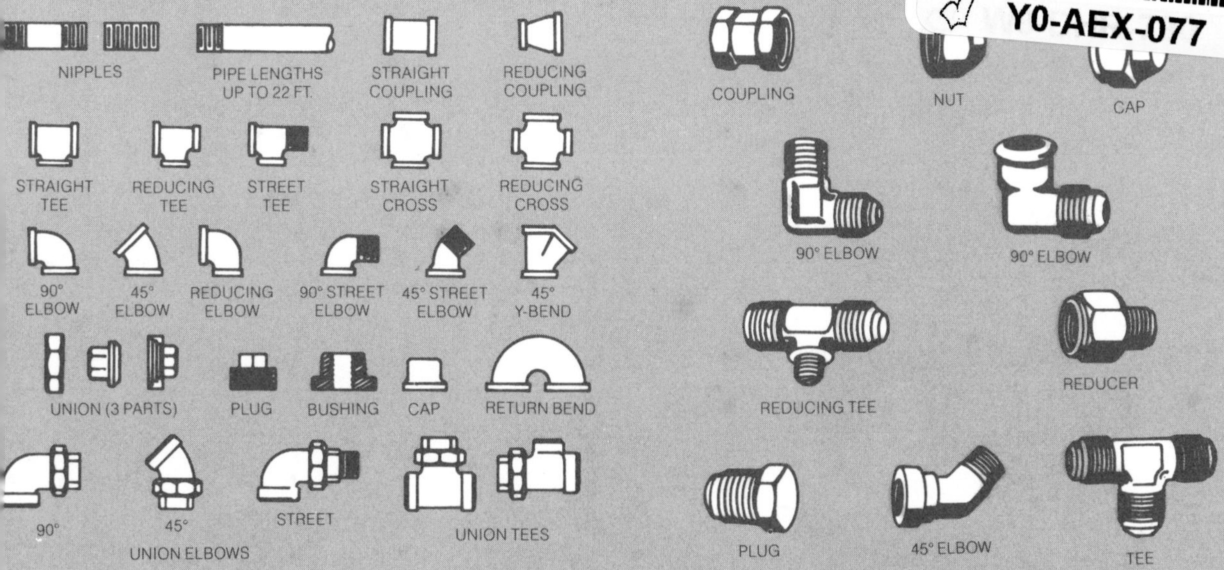

MEASURES OF CAPACITY

1 cup	=	8 fl oz
2 cups	=	1 pint
2 pints	=	1 quart
4 quarts	=	1 gallon
2 gallons	=	1 peck
4 pecks	=	1 bushel

STANDARD STEEL PIPE ((All Dimensions in inches)

Nominal Size	Outside Diameter	Inside Diameter	Nominal Size	Outside Diameter	Inside Diameter
⅛	0.405	0.269	1	1.315	1.049
¼	0.540	0.364	1¼	1.660	1.380
⅜	0.675	0.493	1½	1.900	1.610
½	0.840	0.622	2	2.375	2.067
¾	1.050	0.824	2½	2.875	2.469

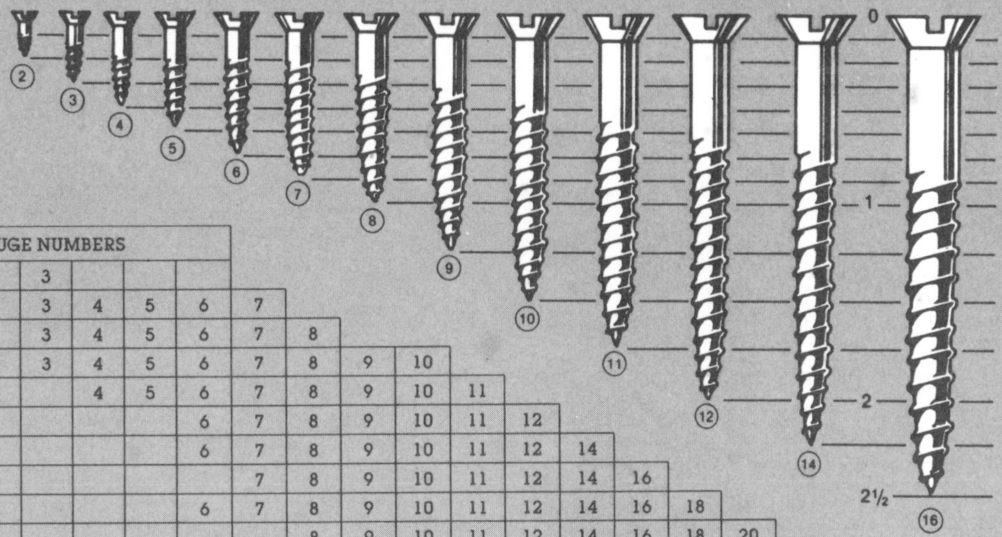

WOOD SCREWS

LENGTH	GAUGE NUMBERS													
¼ INCH	0	1	2	3										
⅜ INCH			2	3	4	5	6	7						
½ INCH			2	3	4	5	6	7	8					
⅝ INCH				3	4	5	6	7	8	9	10			
¾ INCH					4	5	6	7	8	9	10	11		
⅞ INCH							6	7	8	9	10	11	12	
1 INCH							6	7	8	9	10	11	12	14
1¼ INCH								7	8	9	10	11	12	14	16
1½ INCH							6	7	8	9	10	11	12	14	16	18
1¾ INCH									8	9	10	11	12	14	16	18	20
2 INCH									8	9	10	11	12	14	16	18	20
2¼ INCH										9	10	11	12	14	16	18	20
2½ INCH													12	14	16	18	20
2¾ INCH														14	16	18	20
3 INCH															16	18	20
3½ INCH																18	20	24
4 INCH																18	20	24

WHEN YOU BUY SCREWS, SPECIFY (1) LENGTH, (2) GAUGE NUMBER, (3) TYPE OF HEAD—FLAT, ROUND, OR OVAL, (4) MATERIAL—STEEL, BRASS, BRONZE, ETC., (5) FINISH—BRIGHT, STEEL BLUED, CADMIUM, NICKEL, OR CHROMIUM PLATED.

Popular Mechanics

do-it-yourself encyclopedia

The complete, illustrated home reference guide from the world's most authoritative source for today's how-to-do-it information.

Volume 22

SIDING

to

STEREO SYSTEMS

HEARST DIRECT BOOKS

NEW YORK

Acknowledgements

The Popular Mechanics Encyclopedia is published with the consent and cooperation of POPULAR MECHANICS Magazine.

For POPULAR MECHANICS Magazine:

Editor-in-Chief: *Joe Oldham*

Managing Editor: *Bill Hartford*

Special Features Editor: *Sheldon M. Gallager*

Automotive Editor: *Wade A. Hoyt, SAE*

Home and Shop Editor: *Steve Willson*

Electronics Editor: *Stephen A. Booth*

Boating, Outdoors and Travel Editor: *Timothy H. Cole*

Science Editor: *Dennis Eskow*

Popular Mechanics Encyclopedia

Project Director: *Boyd Griffin*

Manufacturing: *Ron Schoenfeld*

Assistant Editors: *Cynthia W. Lockhart, Peter McCann, Rosanna Petruccio*

Production Coordinator: *Peter McCann*

The staff of Popular Mechanics Encyclopedia is grateful to the following individuals and organizations:

Editor: *C. Edward Cavert*

Editor Emeritus: *Clifford B. Hicks*

Production: *Layla Productions*

Production Director: *Lori Stein*

Book Design: *The Bentwood Studio*

Art Director: *Jos. Trautwein*

Design Consultant: *Suzanne Bennett & Associates*

Illustrations: *AP Graphics, Evelyne Johnson Associates, Popular Mechanics Magazine, Vantage Art.*

Contributing Writers: Frank M. Butrick, *Snow removal the easy way*, page 2752; George Campbell, *Pure drinking water from the sun*, page 2772; Victor D. Chase, *Solar energy guide*, page 2761; Howard R. Clark, *Projector stand that rolls away*, page 2715; Karl F. Frank, *Solar water heater you can build*, page 2779; Ed Franzese, *Vacuum cleaner repair*, page 2728; Dan Ramsey, *Small appliance repair*, page 2718; Christopher Greenleaf, *Compact disc players*, page 2810; *Equalizers for your stereo system*, page 2811; Bill Kanner, *Record care: it pays to be tender*, page 2807; Richard Nunn, *Sheathing basics*, page 2697; Mort Schultz, *Siding basics*, page 2692; *Coffee Percolator repair*, page 2725; *Portable food mixer repair*, page 2748; *Food processor repair*, page 2750; Penelope A. Spangler, *Vinyl siding installation*, page 2707; *Snow-melting system you can install*, page 2754; Penelope Spangler and Constance Spates, *Stained glass projects*, page 2790; David A. Warren, *Solar system heat pump-water heater*, page 2784; Harry Wicks, *Residing: you can do it yourself*, page 2700; *Solar garden shed you can build*, page 2768; *Solar water heater installation*, page 2780; *Stairwell to your basement*, page 2804; Robert Wortham, *Stained glass*, page 2787.

Picture Credits: Popular Mechanics Encyclopedia is grateful to the following for permission to reprint their photographs: American Plywood Association, pages 2697, 2698 (right); American Solar King Corp., page 2761; Georgia-Pacific Corp., pages 2692 (top); Hamilton Beach-Scovil, pages 2722 (left), 2750; Cynthia Lockhart, pages 2719 (top and bottom), 2720, 2723 (top left and top right); Masonite Corp., pages 2694, 2700; Norelco—Consumer Products Division—North American Philips Corp., page 2721 (center); Oster—A Division of the Sunbeam Corp., pages 2718, 2721 (top right); Sunbeam Appliance Co., A Division of the Sunbeam Corp., pages 2721 (bottom), 2722 (right), and 2723 (bottom).

ISBN 0-87851-175-X

Library of Congress 85-81760

10 9 8 7 6 5 4 3 2

PRINTED IN THE UNITED STATES OF AMERICA

Contents

Siding basics

QUALITY PLYWOOD siding can approximate the look of vertical cedar siding—especially if the horizontal joints between panels are carefully worked into a house's design as visual elements.

■ SINCE THE MATERIAL you use to re-side your home will probably be with you for a long time, take a few minutes to consider all the possibilities. In this article we'll discuss the relative merits—and demerits—of metal sidings (aluminum and steel), vinyl siding, natural wood, and combination wood and synthetic compound (hardwood and plywood) which we will refer to as sheet siding. Asbestos is not considered since leading manufacturers have discontinued production because of the health problems associated with it. Masonry siding will also be considered a separate topic.

Which is best?

Each siding material has its advantages and disadvantages. The one you choose for your home will probably be selected on the basis of budget, esthetic preference, and/or willingness to put up with certain drawbacks. For example, some homeowners want to avoid painting, no matter what. They shy away from wood and sheet siding and end up paying more money for vinyl or metal. [When speaking about metal siding, we mean aluminum, primarily. However, what is true of aluminum is basically true of steel. Steel siding is stronger than aluminum and offers the advantage of not denting as easily; but it costs 30 to 40 percent more than aluminum and has not been in demand.]

Other homeowners don't think the additional cost is worth the advantages that vinyl and aluminum offer. Furthermore, they want the greater selection of styles and colors afforded by wood and sheet siding.

What about cost?

As matters stand, homeowners have made aluminum the best-selling siding material. Over 10 million homes have been sided with aluminum. Some aluminum siding is not outfitted with backer board, which gives siding more insulating value. The addition of backer board adds to the cost of the job, depending on the type and thickness of the backer board. Be sure that you know exactly what you are going to get for the quoted price.

Vinyl is next in line as the best-selling siding material, with wood and sheet siding following. The cost of contractor-installed vinyl siding is 20 to 30 percent more than aluminum.

There is no way to pinpoint accurately the cost of wood and sheet siding. Cost varies significantly from type to type, from locale to locale and from week to week because of fluctuating building-product prices. Generally, though, the cost of re-siding a home with wood, plywood or hardboard is 25 to 40 percent *less* than re-siding with aluminum.

Hardboard and plywood sidings are comparable in cost with lesser-grade solid lumber materials. However, the cost of superior-grade solid lumber siding is higher than that of sheet siding.

VINYL SIDINGS come in 8-in. (top photo) and double 4-in. lap panels. They are available in several colors, untextured or with a wood-grain texture. Use of backer board (A) under vinyl or aluminum siding increases their insulative value while reducing noise infiltration. There is a wide variety of styles that range from a rough-sawn shingled look in aluminum (B) to a vinyl embossed with a barn-board-like texture (C).

COST INDEX COMPARISON: WOOD AND SHEET SIDING

Type of Siding	Rating
Hardboard, lap or panel, textured	100
Hardboard, lap or panel, smooth	90
⅜" plywood—cedar and southern pine	93
Superior-grade wood drop siding—horizontal and vertical Douglas fir and southern pine	314
Cedar siding, unseasoned and rough-sawn face—vertical siding with battens	100
Tropical hardwood (shorea), bevel siding	314
Cedar hand-split shakes	141

* Calculated using hardboard textured siding as base of 100.

CEDAR SHINGLES? No, they're actually horizontal strips of hardboard embossed to look like courses of shingles. "Courses" are available in 16-ft. lengths.

Wood and sheet types

Hardboard siding is composed of wood fibers that are combined with resins and other synthetic compounds. The materials are permanently bonded under heat and pressure into boards or panels that will withstand exposure to the elements.

Siding made of hardboard is grainless. Where finished panels have a wood-grain appearance,

the grain has been embossed into the panel. In other words, the grain is simulated. Hardboard siding is available unprimed (least expensive), primed (moderately expensive) and prefinished (most expensive). A suitable quality of such siding is at least 7/16 in. thick. The material comes in two general styles: lap (or clapboard) and panel.

Lap denotes boards that are 16 ft. long and of varying widths (6, 9, 12 in. and so forth), which are installed horizontally. The panel style is available in panels measure 4x8, 4x9 and 4x12 ft. or larger. These panels are nailed to a structure so the long dimension runs vertically. The most readily available size is 4x8 ft., however. Longer sizes may have to be specially ordered.

Variety of hardboard siding

Hardboard lap sidings are available several ways:
● Prefinished or primed horizontal clapboard style.
● Unprimed or primed horizontal clapboard style with a simulated rough cedar texture.
● Unprimed simulated wood-shingle siding.
● Primed or unprimed lap siding with a simulated rough-sawn surface.

Similarly, hardboard panel sidings can be bought in the following forms:
● Prefinished or unprimed simulated cypress. Panel edges are shiplapped with ½-in. V-grooves, 8 in. on center, to provide the appearance of individual vertical planks.
● Prestained, primed or unprimed simulated

SIDING: ADVANTAGES AND DISADVANTAGES

	Aluminum	Vinyl	Steel	Hard-board	Ply-wood	Natural Wood (Painted)
No refinishing needed	■	■	■			
Won't split, crack or warp	■	1	■			
Won't blister, peel or flake	■	0	■			
Resists stains	2	2	2, 3			
Won't show scratches	4	■	4			
Won't rot	■	■	■	5		
Resists dents		■	■	■	■	■
Electrically nonconductive	6	■	6	■	■	■
Fire-resistant	■	7	■			
Noiseless	8	■	8	■	■	■
Immune to insects (termites, carpenter ants)	■	■	■			
Comparable ease of installation	Average	Hard	Hardest	Easy	Easiest	Easy

1. Some critics contend that vinyl may crack in extreme cold weather, but others view this as inaccurate.
2. Staining materials usually wash away with rain runoff. If not, a heavy housing may work. Stubborn stains can usually be eliminated with soap and water or household cleaners.
3. If burred edges are present when siding is installed, rust may form.
4. If scratches aren't treated, corrosion (aluminum) or rust (steel) may form.
5. Not usually.
6. Requires grounding.
7. Polyvinyl chloride products are not combustible, but they will smolder and emit toxic gases when in a fire.
8. Critics contend that a metal siding will amplify the noise of rain and hail. However, the use of backer board will reduce the noise level.

ALUMINUM and vinyl manufacturers provide soffits, fascia and trim.

SIDING: INSULATION (R FACTOR)

Material	Resistance (R)
5/16" plywood	.40
3/8" plywood	.48
1/2" plywood	.64
5/8" plywood	.77
7/16" hardboard	.62
.035" vinyl siding and .024" aluminum siding	.87
.035" vinyl siding and .024" aluminum siding with insulating backing material	2.5-6.0*

* Actual insulating value depends on thickness and makeup of backing material, and construction techniques. For example, more air space, thus greater insulating value, is obtained by nailing to furring strips instead of directly to old siding. Thicker backer boards have higher R values; thus polystyrene backer board offers a greater insulating effect than aluminum reflector foil.

A QUALITY JOB includes foam-board insulation and attention given to details. Jamb extenders should always be used to build a window frame so it will extend beyond the new siding surface. The best way to be sure is to inspect at least three jobs by a reputable contractor before you hire him.

rough-sawn cedar with ¾-in.-wide square-cut grooves on 8-in. centers. Also unprimed board-and-batten panels. Battens are integral (they come attached to panels) on 12-in. centers to reduce installation time.

● Primed or prefinished smooth or wood-grained panels with grooves on 8-in. centers or battens on 12-in. centers.

● Prefinished or primed panels having a simulated skip-troweled stucco texture or aggregate stone appearance.

Plywood siding

Plywood siding is a construction of wood veneers that are bonded together with exterior-grade adhesives. The surface of plywood is real wood—not simulated. The siding is manufactured from lumber—usually southern pine, fir or cedar—not from wood fibers as in the case of hardboard.

As with hardboard, plywood siding comes in lap and panel styles: unfinished, primed or prefinished. Varieties are numerous, but not as many as hardboard.

High quality solid lumber siding comes available in clapboard panels and shingles. Surface finishes are grained and rough-sawn.

Metal and vinyl types

Compared to wood and sheet sidings, metal and vinyl sidings come in a limited number of styles. They are virtually maintenance-free and the colors are fast. Painting or staining is not necessary. This fact alone makes metal and vinyl very popular.

At one time, metal had the advantage of outpacing vinyl in the number of colors it offered consumers. It still does, but the gap has closed.

You do not have to settle for the traditional smooth 8-in. or double 4-in. lap panels with vinyl siding. The "woodsy" look (simulated, of course) is available.

Aluminum siding, however, does provide greater versatility than vinyl. In aluminum, you can select from the traditional smooth clapboard look (8-in. or double 4-in.) and from panels having a wood-grain appearance, a rough-sawn surface, vertical board-and-batten or vertical walnut look and hand-split shingle appearance.

Test data demonstrates that metal and vinyl with backer board have greater insulating properties than wood and sheet siding. Assuming that new siding will be applied over existing siding, the chart shown is a summary of relative R values. (The R value denotes the efficiency of insulating materials; higher R numbers have greater resistant to passage of heat.)

Warranty: more than a number

Length of warranty is important, to be sure, but what the warranty covers is just as important.

Let's consider two typical warranties. Both companies make vinyl siding. One warrants that its vinyl siding panels and accessories (soffits, fascia and rain-carrying equipment) are "free from manufacturing defects and won't corrode, blister, peel or flake, won't conduct electricity to require grounding, and won't deteriorate as a result of salt spray, wind-blown sand or termite activity."

It assumes 100-percent responsibility for the first three years. If defective, the siding will be replaced without charge.

In the ensuing 37 years, if a defect is found with this company's siding, the company will contribute the following percentage toward repair or replacement cost: First year, 90 percent; second, 80 percent; third, 70 percent; fourth, 60 percent; fifth, 50 percent; sixth, 40 percent; seventh, 30 percent; 8th through 16th, 20 percent; and for the 17th through 37th, 10 percent.

The other company warrants that its vinyl siding panels are free from peeling, flaking, rusting, blistering, corroding "or other conditions" arising from manufacturing defects. It will assume 100 percent of the cost of repair or replacement during the first five years up to a maximum of $150 per 100 sq. ft. From the 6th through the 10th year, the company will assume 50 percent of the cost up to a maximum of $75 per 100 square feet. From the 11th through the 20th year, the amount of responsibility assumed is reduced by 5 percent each year from the 6th through the 10th year.

The first company's warranty can be transferred to someone who buys your home. The other warranty is nontransferable.

Picking a contractor

If you are having vinyl siding installed, some of the questions you should ask a contractor are:

1. What kind of nail are you going to use? (Answer—Aluminum or another kind of corrosion-resistant nail.)

2. Where will nails be placed? (Answer—Manufacturers provide slots for nails in the siding. Nails will be hidden. Face nailing is not good practice.)

3. How will you make sure that panels are securely tightened? (Answer—Panels should "float" on nails to allow for expansion and contraction.)

4. How will end joints of adjoining panels be joined? (Answer—They will be overlapped about half length of factory notched cutouts to allow for vinyl's movement as temperature changes.)

5. How are you going to get siding attached evenly to a stucco home? (Answer—Furring strips are used and shimed to get an even nailable base.)

EXTERIOR plywood siding/sheathing is single-layer construction. Boards, battens dress it up.

Sheathing basics

■ ABOUT 87 PERCENT of all homes built in the United States every year use some type of sidewall sheathing. Regardless of the type of siding on your home—new or existing—experts recommend that sheathing be used; without it, the house is not as structurally strong, safe and comfortable as one with properly applied sheathing. It forms a wall in itself, it strengthens the framework, and it has a significant insulating and sound-deadening value depending on the type of material used.

Wood sheathing consists of boards up to 8 in. wide with a shiplap or tongue-and-groove construction for added strength and weather resistance. When buying the material for new construction or making repairs, ask your lumber dealer for a quotation on "sheathing-grade" lumber. Through tests it has been determined that wood sheathing applied diagonally (and properly nailed) forms a wall four times as strong as one sheathed horizontally with exactly the same boards. Diagonal sheathing requires a little more material because of the trimming, but its added strength more than offsets the additional cost involved.

Plywood sheathing will add great strength and

INSULATION-BOARD sheathing goes up in big 4 x 8-ft. panels. It is rated for heat-resistance and also offers sound-deadening qualities.

STAPLE GUN helps to install sheathing as well as nails. Manufacturers imprint nailing schedule right on the material.

rigidity to any structure, and plywood also is ideal for shear walls engineered to resist lateral loads. Plywood sheathing produced by mills belonging to the American Plywood Association is marked "Standard INT-DFPA." The most common thicknesses are ⁵⁄₁₆, ⅜, ½, ⅝, ¾ and ⅞ in. The veneer grade is C face, D back and inner plies. When plywood sheathing is used, building paper and diagonal wall bracing can be eliminated. Common smooth 6d nails or annular, spiral-threaded galvanized box nails, or T-nails of the same diameter can be used. Staples can also be used, but at a reduced spacing. If siding such as shingles will be used over the plywood sheathing, you must apply the plywood to the studs with the face grain running across the studs.

Gypsum sheathing has a gypsum-rock core enveloped in a heavy, water-repellent paper. Because of the core, a conventional wall built up with a layer of gypsum sheathing has a fire-resistance rating, depending on the type of construction used. The sheathing is made in sheets ½ x 24 x 96 in., which are quick and easy to install. The tongue-and-groove horizontal edges fit snugly together to reduce wind penetration. The material costs less than wood sheathing. It does have one limitation, however: It can't serve as a nailing base. Wood siding, furring strips and wall ties must be nailed through the sheathing and into the framing members.

Insulation-board sheathing is probably the most common of all sheathing products used today. The material provides more insulation value than competitive sheathing products. Because it is applied over the studs as well as across the spaces between the studs, the sheathing covers the entire wall area with a uniform layer of insulation. It is manufactured from scientifically

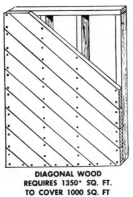

DIAGONAL WOOD
REQUIRES 1350* SQ. FT.
TO COVER 1000 SQ. FT

HORIZONTAL WOOD
REQUIRES 1150* SQ. FT.
TO COVER 1000 SQ. FT.

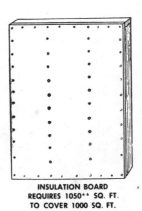

INSULATION BOARD
REQUIRES 1050** SQ. FT.
TO COVER 1000 SQ. FT.

*Includes Dimensional Loss and Estimated Cutting Waste
**No Dimensional Loss with Fiberboard

processed wood or cane fiber. The fiber is reduced to a pulp and reassembled under heat and pressure to form the sheets.

Insulation-board sheathing is produced in two thicknesses: ½ and 25/32 in. Available board sizes are 2 x 8, 4 x 8 and 4 x 9 ft. Other sizes are made on a special-order basis. Two other products are also available: nail-base and intermediate fiberboard sheathing. Intermediate, manufactured in 4 x 8 and 4 x 9-ft. sheets and in ½-in. thickness, eliminates the need for corner bracing in frame construction when it is nailed according to recommendations.

Nail-base sheathing, available in the same sizes as intermediate sheathing, is a high-density product that also eliminates the need for corner bracing frame construction. With nail-base, you can apply wood and asbestos cement shingles directly to the sheathing with annular grooved nails. With regular fiberboard sheathing and ½-in. thick intermediate sheathing, wood furring strips must be used for wood or asbestos cement shingles. You can apply wood shingles to fiberboard shingle backer in combination with any fiberboard sheathing, using annular grooved nails. The wood furring strips can be omitted.

Other features of the material include easy handling, light weight, better workability and better bracing strength. Since the material is water-repellent and forms a weathertight cover,

no building paper is required, resulting in a cost savings.

The sheets of insulating-board sheathing are applied vertically to the walls. When the material is used without corner bracing, staples or nails should be applied to the intermediate studs first, and the fasteners must be spaced not more than 6-in. on center.

Where 2 x 8-ft. sheets of the material are used with tongue-and-groove or shiplap joints, apply it at right angles to the framing members. Supplementary corner bracing is required. The sheathing should be applied with a ⅛-in. space between the ends of the boards. Make sure the interlocking long edges of the boards fit snugly with the tongues up. Nail to the intermediate framing members first with the fasteners spaced 8 in. on center. Nail the vertical edges next, spacing the fasteners 4 in. on center and not less than ⅜ in. from the edge of the sheathing panel.

Shingle-backer board is an insulating material similar to insulating-board sheathing. It is used as a backing for shingles and some types of siding such as aluminum. The material eliminates the need for undercourse shingles, adds insulation value and strengthens and deepens the attractive "shadow line" of the shingles. Backer board is made in sheets measuring 4 ft. long and, depending on the manufacturer, something under 12, 16 or 18 in. wide to undercourse shingles of those sizes.

Re-siding: you can do it yourself

■ MANY HOMEOWNERS GROW TIRED of repainting their houses every few years. They often have an unrewarding experience of having paint blister, peel and scale within two years of painting—despite the hours spent in preparation and painting and the high-quality paint used. If you are among these homeowners, you should think about re-siding rather than painting.

THESE BEFORE-AND-AFTER photos were taken during the first and last weeks of the same month. The old siding (left photo) was cracked and peeling and often needed paint.

WITH ONE SIDE completed, the builder and a friend work their way up the front of the house.

MINERAL SIDING can be worked easily with tools most do-it-yourself enthusiasts have at hand. Shingles come in 4-ft. lengths in your choice of nine colors. Scaffolding makes the job far easier and is well worth rental fee. Without it, some siding jobs would become virtually impossible. A close-up view of the totally prefinished siding (left) shows its attractive wood-grain surface and texture.

WHY THE JOB WAS NECESSARY

A STUDY OF the old clapboard siding makes clear why still another paint job held so little appeal. The same sections of the house, shown with the old siding and the new mineral shingles, show how great a difference can be made by new siding. At the time of these photos, the last paint job was only two years old. It had included a thorough scraping, spot priming with aluminum paint, an alkyd prime coat, topped with an alkyd finish coat. Bays between the studs had been vented. But still the paint cracked and blistered. Quality paint was used throughout—but it failed. The decision for new siding wasn't difficult to make.

GETTING READY FOR THE SIDING

THE FIRST STEP is to remove all attachments such as shutters (left) and the flower box beneath windows (center). Molding at the soffit-wall joint also comes off.

In this instance, workmen replaced that strip of molding with a double layer of wood lath so as to avoid changing the original profile.

APPLYING THE SIDING

STAPLING 15-lb. alphalt-saturated felt over the old siding is the first step in installing the new material. Then nail wood lath below the butt edges of the old clapboards wherever you find them needed to provide a solid nailing base. Next, install corner mold at both ends of the wall run (top, right). To install a corner, drive nails through the trim's flanges into clapboard butt edges. Then apply double lath (lower left) to the lowest clapboard. A backing strip goes under each shingle end joint (bottom, center). A long level or chalkline serves to level the panel (bottom, right) and three nails are driven home. You're on your way.

KICK-STRIP UNDERCOURSE, a special plastic shim strip to get an architectural shadowline under shingle butts (far left), sits atop each course. Just press it down firmly around the top of each shingle panel. To ensure staggered joints, start the first course with a full 48-in. panel. Then second and third courses start with half and quarter lengths respectively (near left).

FITTING SIDING AROUND WINDOWS AND DOORS

BEFORE SHINGLES go on, install J-channel on all casings around windows and doors (drawing, facing page). When you get to a window, you'll have to cut—and maybe notch—a shingle. Hold it in place and mark it for the cutting operation (left and center photos). Doors, as you'd expect, are treated in the same way (right).

SCRIBING INSIDE CORNERS

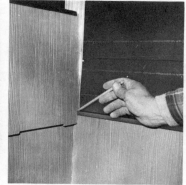
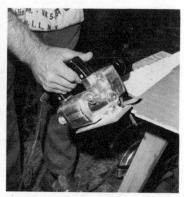

AFTER FELT IS stapled to the existing siding, nail aluminum flashing to inside corners, making a valley for any rainwater seeping into the joint. A corner shingle must be notched for the Kick-Strip it abuts (right). A dust mask would be good to use in cutting shingles; they're sometimes made of asbestos.

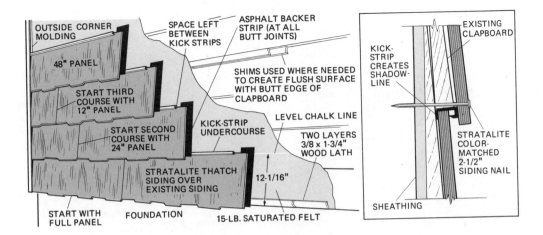

NAIL FIRST J-channel to the sill's underside. Then bobtail the sill ends to accept the vertical channels, which go up next. A spirit level will help the work.

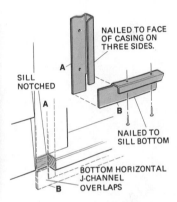

NOTCH all J-channel ends; the horizontal (B) tongue slides into a notch in the vertical piece (A).

A SECOND shingle is held in place and scribed to fit an inside corner.

Factors to consider

There are several points to consider when deciding what kind of siding to install yourself:

You may want your home to have a woodlike appearance that does *not* look factory-made.

Second, the installation procedure has to be realistically within the range of a do-it-yourselfer.

Third, the siding should be prefinished or you'll be doing nothing more than substituting one painting chore for another.

Do-it-yourself

Measure the house for the amount of siding needed. Follow this procedure: Add up the square footage of all outside walls and subtract the footage of doors and windows. Find the num-

WORKING WITH THE MATERIALS

TO CUT metal corner moldings and J-channel notches, use a sabre saw with a hacksaw blade.

STRAIGHT CUT on a shingle is made from back. Carbide-tipped blade in a circular saw does best. Use a mask.

WHEN cutting a shingle, support it fully on a plywood table. Set the blade barely to clear the work.

A CUT SHINGLE-TOP means the Kick-Strip must be trimmed too. Strips must have a gap to allow for thermal expansion. You needn't cut sections for long runs. Just press them onto the shingles after the course is nailed up.

ber of siding squares you'll need from your total, then add 10 percent to compensate for waste. A "square" of siding covers 100 sq. ft.

As the illustrations show, the material is easy to work with, although you must wear a dust mask any time you use a power saw on mineral siding. Some of it contains asbestos cement, and the dust is now recognized as causing cancer.

The trickiest part is putting J-channel around windows and doors. If a neighbor has recently added aluminum siding, check it closely. It probably went on with a similar system. Remember that the bottom horizontal goes *under* the sill, so sill ends must be sawn off to clear the vertical channels. The drip cap at the top comes off, too. J-channel replaces it.

SPECIAL TOUCH-UP paint goes a long way; this little jar was enough to cover all the joints.

Vinyl siding installation

HOUSE, BEFORE SIDING and window installation, needs attention.

■ WHEN IT COMES TIME TO PAINT your house, you may want to choose an alternative—install vinyl siding. Since color goes entirely through the vinyl, your painting days will be over and maintenance will be minimal.

Tools needed

Most of the tools required for a vinyl siding job are already in your shop. One you should purchase when you buy the siding is a snaplock punch. It punches lugs or ears in the cut edges of vinyl siding so the siding can lock into vinyl trim.

Another helpful tool is an unlocking tool. It's a hook that unlocks a panel already in position.

Unless you have a one-story house, you'll want to rent scaffolding. Professionals use a pump-jack-type scaffolding. The safest type for a homeowner, however, is a stationary steel-platform-type scaffolding. You can rent this by the week or month. When you go to the rental outlet, have

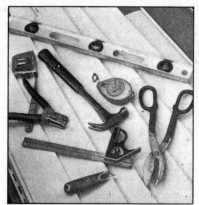

TOOLS INCLUDE a split level, rule, snaplock punch, hammer, chalkline, tin snips, square and utility knife. A fine-tooth power saw (no set, 12 to 16 teeth per in.) helps.

THE SNAPLOCK PUNCH forms ears or lugs in the cut edges of siding used for the top course and around the openings. The punched edge locks into undersill or finish trim.

TO MATCH the brown aluminum gutter and downspout, we bent an aluminum fascia to shape with an aluminum brake. Preshaped vinyl fascia eliminates need for brake.

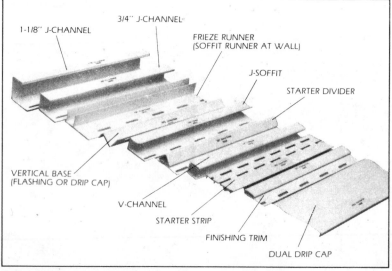

1-1/8" J-CHANNEL
3/4" J-CHANNEL
FRIEZE RUNNER (SOFFIT RUNNER AT WALL)
J-SOFFIT
STARTER DIVIDER
VERTICAL BASE (FLASHING OR DRIP CAP)
V-CHANNEL
STARTER STRIP
FINISHING TRIM
DUAL DRIP CAP

THE VINYL accessories shown are designed to give the project a finished look and to make weather-resistant joints. Inside and outside vinyl corner posts are also needed.

AFTER INSTALLING rigid insulation, snap a chalkline for the starter strip parallel to the top of the foundation wall. Before snapping, check line with a spirit level.

NAIL STARTER STRIP in place with corrosion-resistant nails. Leave a ¼ in. gap between strip and corner post for expansion. Use nails that go ¾ in. into framing.

INSTALL OUTSIDE AND INSIDE corner posts before beginning to side. Nail posts on 12-in. centers in the center of the slots, but not too tight to prevent lateral expansion.

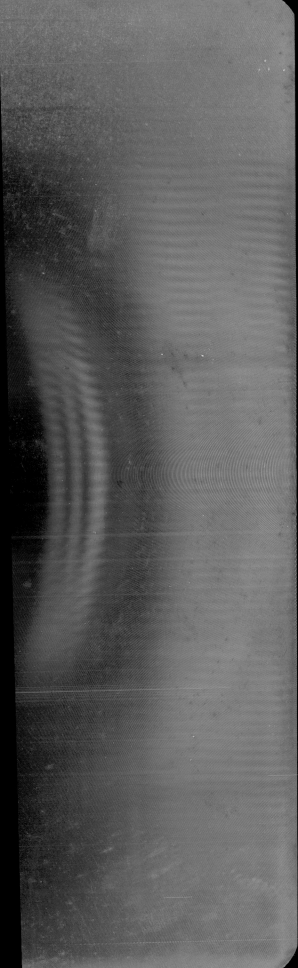

INSTALL THE FIRST PANEL into the interlock of the starter strip. Make sure it's securely locked. Nail every 12 to 16 in., but not so tight that panels can't move.

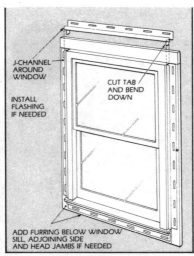

J-CHANNEL AROUND WINDOW

INSTALL FLASHING IF NEEDED

CUT TAB AND BEND DOWN

ADD FURRING BELOW WINDOW SILL, ADJOINING SIDE AND HEAD JAMBS IF NEEDED

AFTER INSTALLING FLASHING at the head (if not already flashed), outline the window with J-channel. You may first have to fur around the window to align panel surfaces.

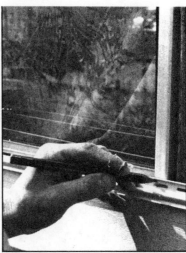

MEASURE THE CUTOUT for the panel that goes under the window. Then cut the panel to opening width, score the panel with a utility knife and snap out the section.

PUNCH LUGS into the cut edge of the siding with a snaplock punch. Then lock a length of finish trim over the cut edge. Here, panel is ready to lock into J-channel.

LOCK THE FINISH TRIM into the J-channel and nail through the slots. At the window head, again cut siding, punch the cut edge, add finish trim and install in J-channel.

PANEL OVER THE GARAGE DOOR is also cut. Lap field cuts under factory ends, but avoid vertical joint alignment. Use scaffolding on a house two or more stories (see text).

TO PROVIDE A TIGHT SEAL around a faucet or other protuberance, seam together two pieces of siding without cutout. With ends overlapping, center seam on object.

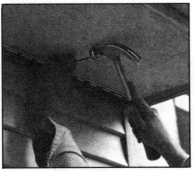

NAIL SOFFIT CHANNELS at the wall and at the fascia edge. Cut soffit panels 1/8 in. shorter than the distance between channels.

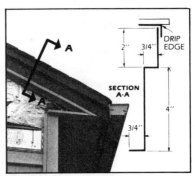

DRIP EDGE

2"   3/4"

SECTION A-A

4"

3/4"

WE BENT aluminum (see drawing) to cover the rake fascia. J-channel is installed below the aluminum fascia. It will hold the finish trim, which covers top courses.

SIDING IS APPLIED above the raised deck in the back of the house. Note that the seams of the rigid insulation are offset.

NEW BAY AND DOUBLE-HUNG WINDOWS are in place. Rigid insulation and siding have been installed on the first floor. Scaffolding will be needed to work on the second floor.

snapshots of the four sides of your house, or a plan drawing. Note length and height of the walls. The salesperson can help determine what you'll need. You should also get information on safe use, including a copy of safety codes such as those developed by the Scaffold Industry Association. Use care when working on scaffolding.

Materials needed

To determine your bill of materials, begin by calculating the amount of siding needed. Add the square footage of all walls, subtract the square footage of the doors and windows and add 10 percent for waste. Siding comes in "squares." Each square is 100 sq. ft. of siding.

For energy conservation, you should consider installing insulation boards over the existing walls before re-siding. Order the same amount of insulation as you order siding. If you plan on siding the soffits, you will also need soffit panels. This material is sold by the square foot.

There are many different types of accessories that you can use, depending on the house structure. Some that you'll definitely need include outside corners, starter strip, J-channel and finish trim. You may also need soffit channel and inside corners. Accessories are sold by the running foot. It is important that you order them properly sized for the siding panels to provide a snug, weatherproof fit. Nails should be aluminum, or at least galvanized or electroplated. They should be long enough to penetrate ¾ in. into the framing or other reliable substrate.

Before you start siding the house, secure and nail any loose boards. Remove downspouts, lighting fixtures, shutters, molding and old caulking around windows and doors. Use furring strips for sidewalls that aren't plumb. Make sure there is adequate attic and crawl-space ventilation and that there are no moisture problems.

Working with vinyl siding

As you work with vinyl siding, keep these points in mind:

• Vinyl siding expands and contracts with the temperature. It must be able to move without binding on the installation nails or against the trim.

• Nail in the center of the slot, but not too tight so that the nail prevents lateral expansion.

• Don't stretch the panels vertically or the end laps will gap.

• Don't nail closer than 10 in. to the end of an overlapping panel to produce neat end laps. Lap panels 1½ in. after cutting off the nailing flange so there is a gap (⅛ in. per 4 ft.) between adjacent panels.

Installing the siding

After preparations are made and the insulation is secured following the maker's directions, begin work by snapping a chalkline to position the starter strip. It's nailed in place about ¼ in. from the corner-post flange. The corner post sets into a length of J-channel with a 90° cutout taken from the center of the nailing flange so you bend the channel to form a corner. The toughest part of siding is fitting panels at openings.

Slide viewer in a coffee table

■ IF YOU SHOOT slides seriously, you need a light box to sort them on. Commercially made slide-sorter boxes are available but they have several shortcomings. For one, they don't hold very many slides. Also, their reddish light gives a false impression of your slides' color. And finally they're not attractive enough to leave out in plain sight between your sorting sessions.

This light box, though, is another story altogether. Its 900-sq.-in. viewing surface can hold more than 200 2x2-in. slides—many more than most people shoot on even the longest vacation. Its light—if you use the recommended fluorescent tubes or their exact equivalents—is the same

5000 K (Kelvin) bluish-white light that professional photographers and engravers use to judge slide color quality.

The bonus here is that this slide viewer has been built into the top of a handsome, modern coffee table.

The lighting of this tabletop is exceptionally

NAILING jig cut from scrap helps align the side pieces with the end section.

RECESS clearance required for rewind mechanism by using a router or a chisel.

ASSEMBLE the table with glue and lagscrews turned into predrilled holes.

MOUNT rewind mechanism to blocks fastened to the end section.

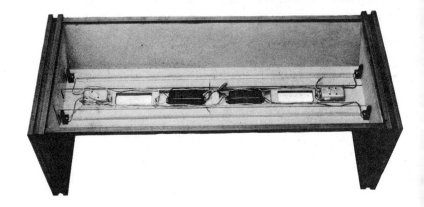

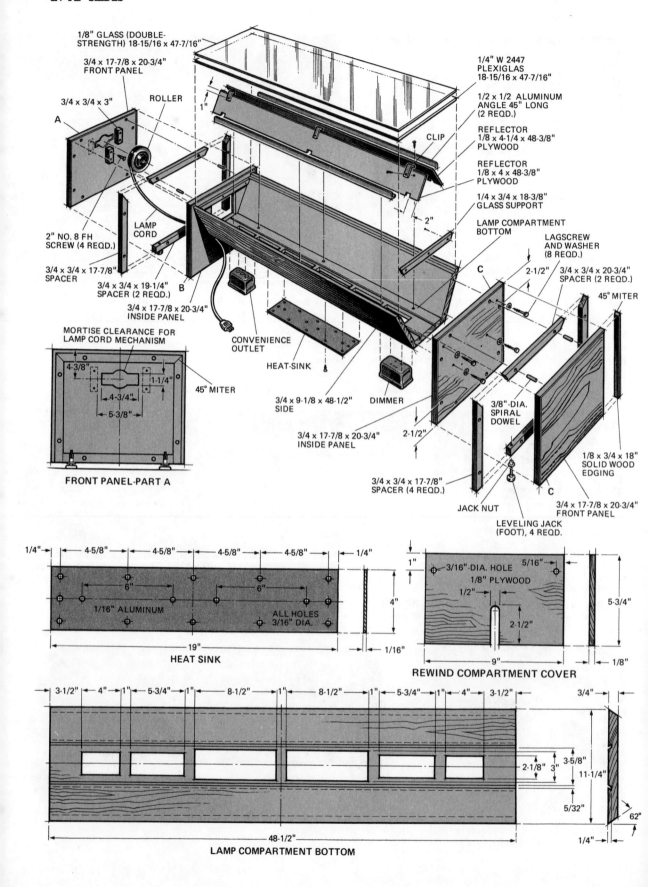

1/8" GLASS (DOUBLE-STRENGTH) 18-15/16 x 47-7/16"

3/4 x 17-7/8 x 20-3/4" FRONT PANEL

3/4 x 3/4 x 3"

ROLLER

A

2" NO. 8 FH SCREW (4 REQD.)

LAMP CORD

3/4 x 3/4 x 17-7/8" SPACER

3/4 x 3/4 x 19-1/4" SPACER (2 REQD.)

B

3/4 x 17-7/8 x 20-3/4" INSIDE PANEL

1/4" W 2447 PLEXIGLAS 18-15/16 x 47-7/16"

1/2 x 1/2 ALUMINUM ANGLE 45" LONG (2 REQD.)

CLIP

REFLECTOR 1/8 x 4-1/4 x 48-3/8" PLYWOOD

REFLECTOR 1/8 x 4 x 48-3/8" PLYWOOD

1/4 x 3/4 x 18-3/8" GLASS SUPPORT

LAMP COMPARTMENT BOTTOM

LAGSCREW AND WASHER (8 REQD.)

2-1/2"

3/4 x 3/4 x 20-3/4" SPACER (2 REQD.)

45° MITER

C

3/8"-DIA. SPIRAL DOWEL

1/8 x 3/4 x 18" SOLID WOOD EDGING

3/4 x 17-7/8 x 20-3/4" FRONT PANEL

2-1/2"

C

JACK NUT

LEVELING JACK (FOOT), 4 REQD.

CONVENIENCE OUTLET

HEAT-SINK

3/4 x 9-1/8 x 48-1/2" SIDE

DIMMER

3/4 x 17-7/8 x 20-3/4" INSIDE PANEL

3/4 x 3/4 x 17-7/8" SPACER (4 REQD.)

MORTISE CLEARANCE FOR LAMP CORD MECHANISM

4-3/8"

1-1/4"

4-3/4"

5-3/8"

45° MITER

FRONT PANEL-PART A

1/4" 4-5/8" 4-5/8" 4-5/8" 4-5/8" 1/4"

6" 6"

1/16" ALUMINUM

ALL HOLES 3/16" DIA.

19"

4"

1/16"

HEAT SINK

1"

3/16"-DIA. HOLE

1/8" PLYWOOD

1/2"

2-1/2"

9"

5/16"

5-3/4"

1/8"

REWIND COMPARTMENT COVER

3-1/2" 4" 1" 5-3/4" 1" 8-1/2" 1" 8-1/2" 1" 5-3/4" 1" 4" 3-1/2"

3/4"

2-1/8" 3" 3-5/8" 11-1/4"

5/32"

48-1/2"

62°

1/4"

LAMP COMPARTMENT BOTTOM

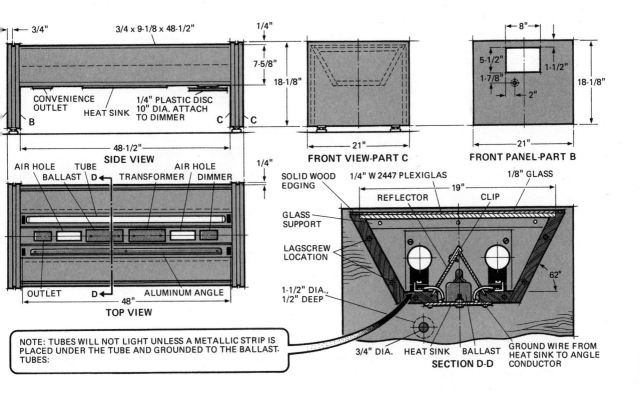

NOTE: TUBES WILL NOT LIGHT UNLESS A METALLIC STRIP IS PLACED UNDER THE TUBE AND GROUNDED TO THE BALLAST. TUBES:

even, thanks to the reflector design which is our version of those used in professional light boxes. We've added two additional features to the professional design: a dimmer—so you can use the light to illuminate glassware and decorative objects with a soft, dramatic glow—and a heavy glass top which lets you set down glasses and the like without fear of scratching the translucent Plexiglas beneath. This feature also lets you put large, unmounted transparencies on semipermanent display between the glass and sheet-acrylic layers.

Notice that neither the glass nor Plexiglas top is provided with finger holes. These can be drilled at both ends if desired. The inside of the box is kept dust-free by eliminating any holes, and using a large suction cup (or tipping the table slightly) whenever it's necessary to remove the glass to change a bulb.

Building the table

Start by laying out all parts on a 4x8-ft. sheet of plywood. Using a portable saw or sabre saw, cut out the parts, making certain that they're slightly oversize. Then recut the pieces to exact size on your table or radial saw using a plywood blade to assure a smooth cut. At this stage, you

should have four endpieces, each 21⁵⁄₁₆-in. wide and 18-in. high. You can also rip the sidepieces to a width of 9¼-in.

Rip the edge strips of solid material of the same species as the plywood used. (On the table shown, birch cabinet-grade plywood was used, so edge strips are of solid birch.) Make each of these edge strips about ⅛-in. thick (this dimension is not critical); then glue to all exposed edges. Next set your tablesaw blade to 28° and bevel one edge of a 1-in.-wide piece of solid stock. This will be used to trim one edge of the side pieces.

Now glue all edge strips to the table ends and sides. During this step, a few well-placed brads will keep the pieces from shifting about during the gluing and clamping operation. If desired, solid edge strips can be eliminated and matching flexible wood tape can be applied using contact cement.

When the glue has dried, use a block plane to remove any excess material and sand the strips perfectly smooth.

Cord rewind mechanism

To get power to the table, we have installed a line on a cord rewind mechanism. The table's hollow and sections are made with a spacer

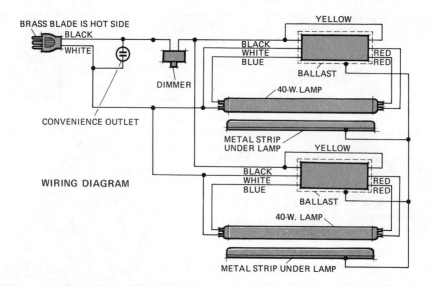

BRASS BLADE IS HOT SIDE
BLACK
WHITE
YELLOW
BLACK
WHITE
BLUE
RED
RED
BALLAST
40-W. LAMP
DIMMER
CONVENIENCE OUTLET
METAL STRIP UNDER LAMP
YELLOW
WIRING DIAGRAM
BLACK
WHITE
BLUE
RED
RED
BALLAST
40-W. LAMP
METAL STRIP UNDER LAMP

around the perimeter as shown. One end contains the rewind mechanism. To assure alignment when gluing up the ends, use dowels as we did. Dowel locating pins make aligning the dowels easier. Notice that the inner end pieces are attached to the slanted side sections before the ends are assembled. By using lagscrews and glue, you are assured of a very strong, tight joint. Make certain that you install washers beneath lagscrew heads.

Make the bottom panel next. Locate and cut the openings as shown; miter the sides and cut the grooves for the reflector.

Before closing in the end containing the rewind mechanism, pass the cord through the opening. To prevent the cord from retracting into the compartment, either install the plug or tie a temporary knot.

The plug used must be either a polarized or grounded type. A polarized plug has one wide and one narrow blade. Be sure to connect the black wire from the dimmer (and transformer) to the brass side of the plug.

If a grounded-type plug should be used, you can follow the same procedure but ignore the green terminal of the plug.

About the light

In order for rapid-start fluorescent tubes to function, they must be placed near a metallic surface. In conventional fixtures, this is accomplished by the metal reflector. Here, because the system is of wood, a metal strip must be placed under the tubes. You can do this with a piece of flat aluminum under the tubes. Or run a strip of electrical conducting tape from one end of each tube to the other. Do not, however, allow the tape to come in contact with the tube pins. If aluminum strip is used, run a piece of wire from it to the transformer base.

Wire the convenience outlet to the hot side of the line before it enters the switch to permit it to function independently. Be sure to solder leads to reel terminals.

To insure a perfectly level table, a set of levelers should be installed under the corners.

Projector stand that rolls away

■ SETTING UP for a slide or movie show can be a bothersome chore if you have to drag the projector out of a closetful of clutter, find a table to put it on, then go searching for those stray film reels or slide trays. This mobile projection stand solves the problem by keeping everything at your fingertips. You just roll it out, set the projector on top, and you're ready.

The wheeled cart is roomy enough to store both a slide and movie projector, plenty of trays or reels, extra editing equipment and even a tape recorder for adding sound to your presentations. The top surface puts the projector at a height of about 32 inches—a convenient working level that lets you operate it comfortably from a sitting position.

The slickest feature of all is a built-in, slope-front control panel that slides out like a drawer from one end. The panel contains three switched power outlets and a back-lighted slide viewer for checking and editing your transparencies. The outlets enable you to plug in not only the projector but additional equipment like a tape recorder and a floor or table lamp. With a lamp plugged in, you can control room illumination yourself without having to ask someone else to turn the lights on and off every few minutes.

When not in use, the cart rolls out of the way against a wall and can double as a dining room sideboard, mobile snack bar or roll-around stand for a portable TV set. Decorative clear-plastic casters make good wheels since they're trim-looking.

For a rich appearance, use hardwood-veneered plywood for the top, sides and doors,

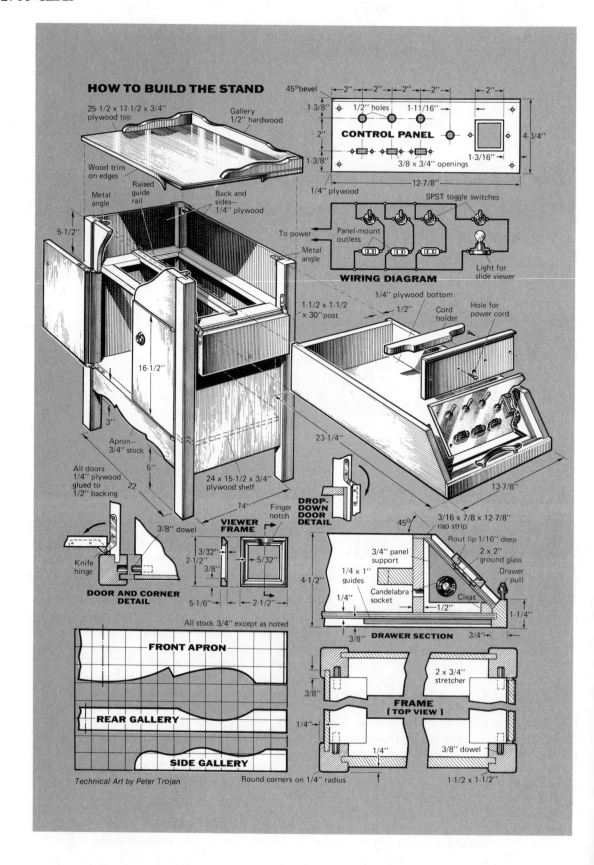

HOW TO BUILD THE STAND

25-1/2 x 17-1/2 x 3/4''
plywood top

Gallery
1/2'' hardwood

Wood trim
on edges

Metal
angle

Raised
guide
rail

Back and
sides—
1/4'' plywood

5-1/2''

Metal
angle

16-1/2''

1-1/2 x 1-1/2
x 30'' post

1/4'' plywood bottom

1/2''

Cord
holder

Hole for
power cord

3''

Apron—
3/4'' stock

5''

22

24 x 15-1/2 x 3/4''
plywood shelf

14''

All doors
1/4'' plywood
glued to
1/2'' backing

3/8'' dowel

**VIEWER
FRAME**

Finger
notch

**DROP-
DOWN
DOOR
DETAIL**

23-1/4''

13-7/8''

Knife
hinge

**DOOR AND CORNER
DETAIL**

3/32''
2-1/2''
3/8''

5/32''

5-1/6''   2-1/2''

All stock 3/4'' except as noted

45°

3/16 x 7/8 x 12-7/8''
cap strip

Rout lip 1/16'' deep

2 x 2''
ground glass

3/4'' panel
support

Drawer
pull

1/4 x 1''
guides

1/4''

Candelabra
socket

Cleat

4-1/2''

1-1/4''

3/8''

DRAWER SECTION

3/4''

1/2''

CONTROL PANEL

45° bevel

2'' 2'' 2'' 2''   2''

1-3/8''

1/2'' holes   1-11/16''

2''   4-3/4''

1-3/8''

3/8 x 3/4'' openings   1-3/16''

12-7/8''

1/4'' plywood

SPST toggle switches

To power

Panel-mount
outlets

Light for
slide viewer

WIRING DIAGRAM

FRONT APRON

REAR GALLERY

SIDE GALLERY

Technical Art by Peter Trojan

Round corners on 1/4'' radius

2 x 3/4''
stretcher

FRAME
(TOP VIEW)

3/8''

1/4''

1/4''

3/8'' dowel

1-1/2 x 1-1/2''

BASIC POST-AND-RAIL frame is shown in the photo at right. The grooves in the corner posts for back and side panels are blind, extending only part way down so they won't show where the legs are exposed. Setup for cutting these grooves on a dado head is shown above. Mark the fence to indicate blind end of post, then drop the post over blade at this point and feed it forward.

with matching solid stock for the leg posts, apron and gallery strips. You can build up the ¾-inch thickness for the top, front and doors by gluing ¼-inch veneer plywood to a ½-inch backing of plain plywood. This trick will let you cut all the outer faces from the same ¼-inch sheet used for the side and back panels, saving the cost of a ¾-inch sheet. Birch is a good choice since it is readily available and less expensive than fancier hardwood plywoods, yet can be finished to simulate almost any wood tone you desire.

Cut the main doors and front panel from a single piece of plywood and do the same for the drop-down side door and the panel below it. This way, when the pieces are assembled, you'll get an unbroken flow of grain for a neat, professional appearance. The exposed edges of the top and doors can be concealed with wood tape. The scalloped edges on the apron and gallery give the cart an Early American appearance. If you have a preference for a more modern style, you can omit the curlycues.

The four corner posts are grooved to take the edges of the side and back panels for a sturdy construction. The grooves are ¼ inch wide and ⅜ inch deep and can be cut on a table saw with a dado head set to a ¼-inch width. Note that they're blind, stopping five inches from the

lower ends of the posts so they won't show where the legs are exposed. To cut them accurately, measure five inches from the rim of the dado blade toward the rear of the saw table and mark this point on the fence. Align the blind end of each post with this mark on the fence and carefully lower the post onto the blade, making a pocket cut. Continue the cut by feeding the post forward to complete the groove. This way, all four posts will come out identically grooved. By hand, chisel out the rounded ends of the grooves left by the curved blade so the cuts are square throughout their length.

Use offset knife hinges so the doors will swing fully open without binding. The drop-down door that hides the control panel must be carefully positioned so it clears the drawer in the open position, but makes a snug fit when it's closed. The toggle switches and panel-mount outlets are standard radio parts available at electronics-supply houses. The slide viewer is illuminated by a small 7½-watt nightlight bulb in a candelabra socket. Note that there's a finger notch cut out at the top of the viewer frame. This makes it easy to lift slides out of the frame's recess. When not in use, the power cord for the control panel is kept neatly coiled around a cleat inside the drawer so it's out of the way.

Small appliance repair

■ TODAY'S DISPOSABLE SOCIETY has been spoiled by low-cost small appliances. They work simply and well; they are economical to replace. So when the toaster doesn't toast or the mixer doesn't mix, we often go shopping for one that does. And there's nothing wrong with that, except we miss the opportunity to learn something about the gadgetry that permeates our lives,

as well as learn something about ourselves. For many consumers and do-it-yourselfers, small appliance repair is more a question of independence than of economics.

This section in your *Popular Mechanics Do-It-Yourself Encyclopedia* will introduce you to the basics of small appliance repair so you can best make the decision: fix it or toss it. You'll learn the types of small appliances, how to find parts and service information, how to troubleshoot and repair, how to perform preventive maintenance and more.

Types of small appliances

Small appliances can be categorized by one of two functions: they heat something or they move something.

SELECTOR BUTTONS on blenders and food processors control mixing-speed; up to 21 speeds are available on some models.

Small heating appliances include the broiler, coffeemaker, waffle baker or iron, deep fryer, frying pan, electric wok, egg cooker, bottle warmer, corn popper, griddle, grill, clothes iron, roaster and toaster. There are many more. But they all have the same common element: they heat something.

A small motor does the work in ice cream makers, knife sharpeners, fans, vacuum cleaners, mixers, food processors and blenders.

Appliances of both types share a common feature: they must be controlled. In fact, this is often where things go wrong. The pop-up toaster is controlled by a push-down lever hooked to a bimetal thermostat. The food processor's motor speeds are selected through selector buttons. The clothes iron's heat is chosen by a sliding rheostat. Newer small appliances incorporate microprocessor chips for more sophisticated control.

Repair resources

One of the biggest repair mistakes made by do-it-yourselfers is taking the thing apart, spreading the parts out on the kitchen table—then searching for the instruction manual. Most manuals contain the needed information, yet lie unopened in a kitchen drawer. A good instruction manual will present not only the principles of operation and maintenance instructions, but also offer vital parts information and numbers that can help you in ordering and quickly receiving the correct replacement part. Drawings can help you disassemble and reassemble smaller parts. Some instruction manuals will even present troubleshooting guides that will help you select the correct repair and parts without opening the unit.

There are three sources to consider for the parts you need to restore a nonoperative small appliance: factory-authorized service centers, the factory parts distributor and the independent parts house. The authorized service center is an independent business usually serving one appliance manufacturer, while the distributor is linked directly to the factory. A parts house is an independent business and offers replacement parts for a variety of appliances. Most also offer technical assistance with repairs and sell special tools you might need.

A key to using any small appliance repair resource is knowing the make and model of your appliance. In most cases, this information is found on the manufacturer's nameplate on the back or underside of the appliance. Typical nameplate information includes the manufacturer's or retailer's name and location, appliance model number, serial number, power rating in watts, amperage, voltage, standards met (such as UL for Underwriters Laboratory) and important safety statements ("Disconnect toaster before opening to clean out crumbs").

MAKE AND MODEL NUMBER are usually found on manufacturer's nameplates, along with other information useful in getting repair or parts. Look under the appliance for the nameplate.

Repair tools

You probably have most of the hand tools needed to make simple repairs on many small appliances. A basic set will include flat and Phillips screwdrivers, an adjustable wrench or set of smaller wrenches, a pair of pliers and a pocket knife. The job can be made easier with a set of nut drivers (screwdrivers with nut socket heads) and a wire cutter/crimper tool. Small files and a hole punch can also be useful in making minor repairs.

Small appliance maintenance and repair should also include some cleaning. A one-inch soft paint brush and a can of compressed air are very helpful when cleaning crumbs from toasters and dust clots from around wiring, and for drying parts soaked in a cleaner.

Electrical testing requires more specialized tools, but most are available at low cost. The most popular are the continuity tester and the volt-ohm-meter (VOM). The continuity tester includes a light that indicates when electricity is flowing through it from one wire to the other. By carefully placing one lead on each side of a "live" component, you can find out if electricity is actually getting through. A VOM will also tell you how much resistance to electricity flow the component has when tested without power.

Repair safety

Electricity can help you or it can hurt you. Hook it up to a motor and it can open a can or blend food. Touch two live wires and it can knock you across a room—or worse. Keep in mind that just because you can't see electrons flowing through the wire doesn't mean they won't "bite" when mishandled. Here are some simple rules that will make small appliance repair safer.

• Don't work on any electrical appliance or circuit when it is live or attached to an electrical source. In most cases, this simply means unplugging the appliance when making repairs. Some built-in appliances, however, may be wired directly into house wiring. In this case, find the circuit that controls it and turn it off at the main power box. Then use a neon tester or VOM to verify that it is off.

• Don't touch wires that are live. Keep screwdriver tips out of toaster elements and wall plugs. Don't try to get a stalled motor going by turning the armature by hand. This is basic, but something we can forget about unseen electricity.

• Don't become an electrical path. Electricity will move from the power source to the appliance and then return to the source via the "ground." In most cases, ground is a separate wire that offers an electrical path of least resistance. If you are standing on a wet cement floor, however, you could become the path to ground and be shocked.

• Select and use safe electrical parts and equipment. The most common is the electric cord with the UL label. The UL label means that the Underwriters' Laboratories, Inc. standards are followed. UL is an independent firm that formulates standards for manufactured materials for electrical use. UL standards conform to those in the National Electrical Code established by the National Board of Fire Underwriters.

In checking for electrical troubles, it is helpful to imagine that electric current flows through wires like water through pipes. The path traveled by electric current is called a *circuit*. Imagine a circle. When you plug a small appliance (such as a toaster) into the wall socket, electric current flows from one of the two holes, through the corresponding plug prong, up through the attached cord, to the toaster control and heating element, then back out the other wire, through the prong to the outlet and back to the source. Electricity can flow only when the circuit is completely closed, like a circle. A plugged-in toaster is an open circuit until the lever is pressed and the electrical circuit is closed. Then electricity flows and the bread is heated. But even in an open circuit, electricity is in the toaster, stopped at the point of the open switch. Give that electricity a chance to make a complete circuit with a misplaced finger or screwdriver and it will!

Troubleshooting appliance cords

The most common problem faced in repairing small appliances is the electric cord. The electric cord delivers and returns electric current to the appliance. In most cases, it is the easiest appliance component to get at and test. It is also the most abused. Appliances are unplugged with a tug and plugs are assaulted with cleaners, chemicals and heat. Cords become brittle and develop gaps or openings in the wiring or in the coverings insulating one wire from another. Fortunately, cords are easy to test with a VOM. Simply unplug the appliance and attach one lead to one of

DAMAGED ELECTRIC CORDS is the most common problem in repairing small appliances. Cords often become brittle and frayed due to careless unplugging and cleaning. They are easily tested with a VOM and easily replaced when necessary.

the prongs on the plug and the other lead to the bare end of the corresponding wire inside the appliance and measure resistance. Low resistance (a few ohms) means the wire is a good conductor; high resistance (a thousand or more ohms) indicates a break in the wire that will now allow current to pass. Remember to check both prongs and corresponding wires for resistance. Test across both prongs to see if there is a short. You should get some resistance reading because of the motor windings or heater coils, but very low resistance probably means the current is finding a return path before it gets to these higher-resistance parts. When you test, move the plug and cord around to see if there is an intermittent break or short in the wire.

Electrical cords can be easily replaced. Replacement cords are available with attached or separate plugs at most hardware stores. Be sure to replace your cord with one that is similar or better in construction, function and rating. For appliances that draw more than 5 amps, the special, heavier gauge heater cord is preferred.

HEAT IN RESISTANCE–HEATING APPLIANCES is developed by passing current through a special type of wire that has high resistance to the passage of the current. Overcoming this resistance causes heat.

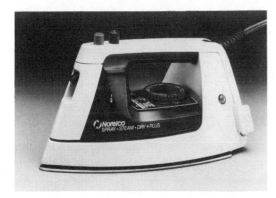

TOASTERS, COFFEE MAKERS AND IRONS have a common element: they all heat something by converting electric energy to heat.

Troubleshooting heating appliances

Resistance-heating appliances convert electrical energy into heat. This heat is then used to toast bread, grill hamburgers, warm a room or deep-fry doughnuts. Heat is developed by passing current through a special type of wire that has high resistance to the passage of current. Overcoming this resistance causes heat. Problems occur in heating appliances when the heating element is damaged or otherwise won't allow electrons to flow through it in a continuous circuit. The primary test of a defective heating appliance is called the *continuity test*. It can be done on a cord, a heating element or a control using an

ohmmeter or VOM. Every electrical circuit must have continuity; that is, the electrical path along the wires and heating elements must not be broken. There must be a continuous circuit from one side of the a.c. line, through the cord, through the switch, through the heating element or motor, and back through the cord to the other side of the a.c. line. The continuity test uses the voltage from a battery inside the VOM to send a current through the tested component, then tells you how much resistance it faced along the path. By

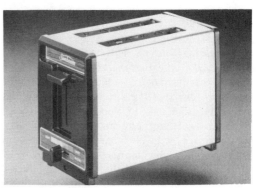

SMALL APPLIANCES, particularly heating appliances such as toasters should be periodically cleaned inside and out to dislodge particles of food that can short out electric circuits.

matching this information with what the circuit resistance should be, you can tell what and where the problem is. A small break in the thin heating wires of an appliance will often interrupt the flow of current as the element expands with heat, making testing both difficult and dangerous.

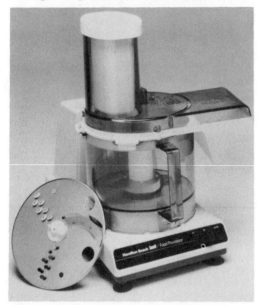

THE ELECTRIC MOTOR in a food processor is specifically designed to move its cutting blades.

Troubleshooting motor appliances

A variety of small electrical appliances moves something with a motor. Food blenders move cutting blades; mixers move beaters; vacuum cleaners move suction blowers; humidifiers move fan blades. Electric motors are usually designed for a specific use. For example, the motor used in an electric mixer would not be suitable for use in a garbage disposer.

All troubles encountered with electric motors can be traced to either mechanical or electrical problems. Mechanical troubles range from minor problems that cause a harmless but annoying noise, to a frozen mechanical shaft that completely locks the motor. To check for mechanical problems, disconnect the motor from both the power and whatever it is driving: blades, gears, etc. Then rotate the motor shaft by hand to make sure it rotates freely. Next check the end play by pushing and pulling the motor shaft back and forth. There should be only a slight amount of end play. Finally, check the motor mountings, especially if the complaint is noise. Look for loose or weak springs, and deteriorated rubber mountings that let the motor vibrate or bind. Re-

place parts as needed using the parts list in your instruction manual or the guidance of a reputable parts retailer.

If electrical troubles with the motor are suspected, the motor should be tested electrically while in the circuit. Most electrical problems are traced to associated circuits rather than to the motor. With the motor out of the appliance, check for resistance between each motor terminal and the frame to see if there is an electrical leak in the windings. Short out the motor capacitor and check it for correct resistance. More complex electrical tests should be made by a qualified technician. If you know the motor is faulty, remove it for bench testing by an electrical repair shop. Some older motors can be opened for service, such as replacing brushes and armature. Most newer motors, however, are replaced as a unit.

TROUBLESHOOTING GUIDES for food mixers and other small appliances on the following pages will help you save time and money by doing minor repairs at home.

Troubleshooting controls

Many small appliances are automatic—that is, they will go through a complete cycle of operation before there is any need for you to do anything. Once the toaster is set for the desired shade of toast and the bread is lowered into the toaster, it operates automatically until done. During the operating cycle, automatic appliances are controlled by thermostats, relays, timers, microprocessors or other devices that control the operating sequence of contacts and switches. These controls are often a hybrid mechanical and electrical system. Troubleshooting and repair is not as complex as it might seem.

Switches include single and multiple contact points. Flicking a switch may activate one or

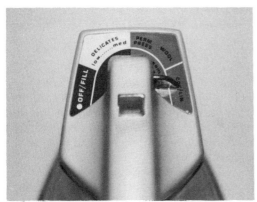 

ALL TYPES OF APPLIANCES must be controlled. In an automatic appliance, this is done by thermostats, relays, timers or microprocessors.

more electrical components. Troubleshooting a switch first requires that you inspect it for mechanical problems: dirty contacts, loose wires, broken throw or other components. Then check it electrically. Use an ohmmeter to decide whether each circuit is operating correctly. Make sure that contacts that are normally closed or normally open really work the way they're supposed to.

Thermostats work by heat. They are used to turn circuits on and off or to activate some mechanical device. Most are controls to maintain a desired temperature level. Some thermostats can be adjusted to correct for wear error. Others should be replaced. Use a match to see whether a thermostat is operating at all. Replace rather than try to repair a defective thermostat.

Mechanical relays depend on some lever action to open or close electrical contacts. For example, inserting a pencil in an electric sharpener moves a lever to close the contacts to start the motor. Electrical relays depend on an electromagnet to move electrical contacts in and out of the circuit. Relays can stick open or closed and cause circuit problems. Problems are caused when contacts are fused together by the heat of electricity or when food or other debris becomes lodged between the contacts, preventing them from operating.

Electrical controls can best be tested using an ohmmeter to decide whether the current is flowing through the unit properly. Mechanical troubleshooting requires that you watch the operation as it works and apply mechanical logic to see if there is some obvious obstruction.

Repair techniques

Once you've discovered the source of your small appliance's problem and decided to repair

it yourself, you need to think about taking it apart and putting it back together. Of course, these should be considered together to make sure you don't have parts left over when you're done.

First thing to remember in disassembly is that the appliance body was designed for three basic purposes: to hold parts together, to protect you from electrical or mechanical hazards and to be decorative. Because it does have to be nice-looking, you can understand why unsightly screws

ELECTRIC PENCIL SHARPENERS usually depend on a mechanical relay. Inserting a pencil moves a lever to close electrical contacts and start the motor.

and clips that hold it together are often hidden under the decoration. Disassembly screws may be under the nameplate or trim, on the bottom of the appliance, under some cover or buried deep in holes. Look for them there. Remember, however, that small appliances are designed for manufacturing and not repair. Disassembly screws or clips, therefore, may be under a glued-on trim plate.

The first rule of small appliance repair is *take your time*. Look over the appliance and consider how it must have been put together at the factory. Take notes on what parts go where and put screws in labeled containers. An egg carton is excellent for storing small parts. Use the pages of your owner's manual to make assembly notes and drawings. Components can be easily bent or broken—usually ones that are difficult to replace.

If you've taken your time in the disassembly of your small appliance, putting it back together should present no special problems. In fact, since small appliances are designed to be manufactured, assembly should be much easier. A few notes, however: Make sure you don't pinch any electrical wires as you assemble your appliance. Check all electrical connections to make sure they are tight. Stop every few minutes and look over the parts you have left to make sure that you are not ahead of yourself and leaving something out. Take an extra few moments to clean parts as you reassemble them.

Preventive maintenance

Here are a few preventive maintenance tips to help you minimize small appliance repair and lengthen the time between repairs.

• Remember that an electrical cord is designed as a conductor of electricity, not as a rope to be pulled. Always grasp the cord at the plug and gently pull it from the socket. Don't yank the plug out of the outlet by pulling on the cord. Be careful where the cord is placed. Never run an electrical cord under a rug where traffic can fray the insulation cover and allow sparks to start a fire. Don't run a cord through a window or other sunlit area without adequate cover. Plastic can deteriorate with excessive sunlight. Also, be careful that you don't run kitchen appliance cords over the burners on your range.

• Another enemy of electricity and small appliances is water. Water can become a good conductor and allow electricity to take a new path to ground, injuring people or damaging property in the path. This is especially a problem when using small appliances around metal sinks that are grounded to pipes. If an appliance does get wet, carefully unplug it or throw the circuit breaker, remove and dry the appliance, and clean up the spill and its source.

• Motors develop heat. Most motors are self-cooling as heat is driven away by the turning motion. This heat, however, must have a way of escaping through vent slots that are clear of obstructions. Check your motorized small appliance to make sure that dust and dirt or other debris is not covering the vent slots, causing the motor to overheat.

• Heating small appliances gather dust and dirt around coils. But you must be extremely careful in cleaning around heating coils. They become brittle with age and can easily break with only the slightest abuse. Use a small vacuum cleaner, fine soft paint brush or can of dry compressed air to clean around heating coils.

• Periodically clean small appliances inside and out. This is especially important with heating appliances such as toasters and waffle irons. Particles of food become lodged in the mechanism and can easily short out electric circuits. Controls become jammed. Heating elements develop hot spots that quickly short-circuit and fail. Remember to use the trap at the bottom of the toaster to periodically clean out crumbs and other foods. Also clean off the back edge of waffle irons where excess batter can hide.

Do-it-yourself small appliance repair

The most common and most used small appliances include the coffee percolator, vacuum cleaner, toaster, clothes iron, food mixer and food processor. The maintenance and repair of these appliances is presented in the following articles. There are, however, dozens of other small appliances that also need maintenance and repair. Fortunately, they are all related to the two small appliance types: heating and motorized.

Coffee percolator repair

■ GOT A PROBLEM with an electric coffee per-colator? Consult the troubleshooting chart to pinpoint possible causes. Then proceed to find the pertinent section which may be used as a guide in making repairs.

Replacement parts can usually be obtained from a dealer selling your make of appliance. If there is no dealer in your area, contact the manu-

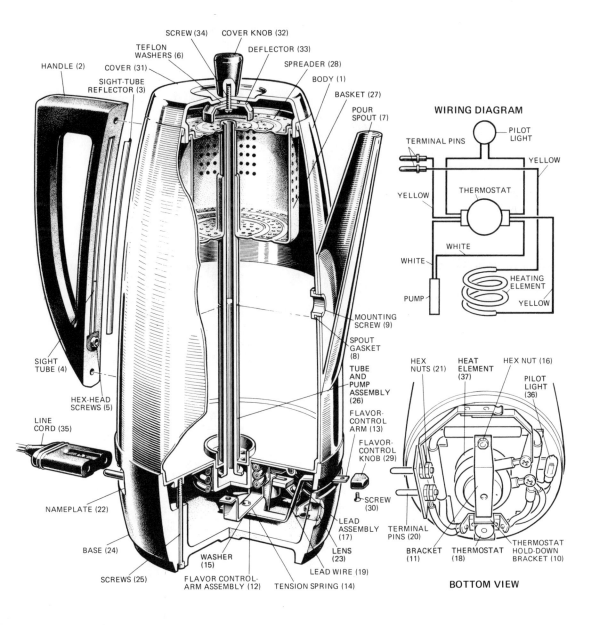

WIRING DIAGRAM

BOTTOM VIEW

facturer. The address is normally stamped on the bottom of the percolator's base.

In the instructions which follow, numbers in parentheses correspond to those on the main illustration for easy identification of parts.

Caution: Except for specific tests requiring power, be sure to disconnect the percolator before doing any work on it.

Replacing the pour spout (7)

1. Remove the mounting screw (9) and spout gasket (8) holding the pour spout (7) to the percolator's body (1).

2. Replace the pour spout with a new one, making certain you install the spout gasket to prevent leakage around the spout.

Possible difference: Spouts of some coffee per-

Coffee tastes bitter

POSSIBLE CAUSE	WHAT TO TRY
1. Residue and stains.	Periodically clean all coffeemaking parts and the inside of the percolator with a cleaner made for electric coffee percolators which is sold in hardware stores, home supply centers and supermarkets. Follow instructions on the package.

Water boils, but does not percolate

POSSIBLE CAUSES	WHAT TO TRY
1. Percolator tube and pump assembly not seated.	Make sure that the pump portion (base) of the percolator tube and pump assembly is seated in the heater well in the body.
2. Percolator tube and pump assembly is bent or pump portion is inoperative.	Replace the percolator tube and pump assembly.

Coffee is too weak or too strong

POSSIBLE CAUSE	WHAT TO TRY
1. Reduced percolating time.	Make certain the percolator is being filled with cold water—never with hot water. Hot water will reduce percolating time.
2. Slow percolating action.	See that the inside of the heater well in the body and the bottom of the percolator tube and pump assembly are free of coffee grounds and deposits that will slow percolating action.
3. Defective thermostat.	Test the unit by removing the percolator tube and the pump assembly and then filling the unit with cold water. Insert a thermometer and connect the percolator to an electrical outlet. The thermostat should open at 180° to 195° F., which is signified by the pilot coming on. If the thermostat should open sooner (or later), replace the thermostat.

Unit does not heat

POSSIBLE CAUSE	WHAT TO TRY
1. No voltage at the receptacle.	Check the receptacle with a table lamp or voltage tester.
2. Line cord has gone bad.	Replace any line cord that has frayed insulation. Check the cord for continuity. A bad cord should be replaced with one of the same size as that originally used by the percolator's manufacturer.
3. Badly corroded or burned terminals, pins.	Try cleaning the terminal pins with a small piece of sandpaper. If this doesn't work, replace the pins.
4. Defective thermostat.	Replace the thermostat.
5. Defective heating element.	Replace the heating element.

colators are a molded part of the body and cannot be replaced.

Replacing the handle (2) and sight tube (4)

1. From inside the body (1), remove the hex-head screws (5) and Teflon washers (6) holding the handle and sight-tube assembly.

2. Lift off the handle and sight-tube assembly and disassemble the handle (2), sight tube (4) and sight-tube reflector (3).

3. Replace the damaged part or parts and prepare for reassembly by placing sight-tube parts in correct sequence into the groove in the handle.

4. Place the entire assembly against the percolator's body, lining up the assembly with the screw holes.

5. Insert screws and washers and tighten the handle and sight-tube assembly to the body.

Caution: Make sure Teflon washers are used to prevent leakage around holes.

Possible differences:

1. Some units do not possess sight tubes.

2. Handles of some units are held by a screw at the top of the handle only. The bottom of the handle is released from its seat by inserting a screwdriver beneath the metal bracket-type clip and prying outward. To replace, press the bracket-type clip into place and insert the screw into the top part of the handle.

3. Handles of some other units cannot be replaced. The handle is a molded part of the body.

Replacing the base (24)

1. Invert the percolator and remove the screw (30) holding the flavor-control knob (29). Remove the knob.

2. Remove the two screws (25) holding the base to the bottom of the percolator.

3. Slowly lift the base up, tipping it to the side slightly so the flavor control arm (13) slides through the slot in the side of the base, which is covered by the nameplate (22).

4. Take the pilot light from the lens (23).

5. Remove the hex nuts (21) securing leads to terminal pins (20). Damaged parts may now be replaced.

Possible differences:

1. Some percolators do not have a flavor-control knob.

2. Some percolators that do have a flavor-control knob do not have knobs held by screws. They are pressed on the flavor-control lever and are removed by pulling them off.

3. Bases of some percolators are held by a single screw that may or may not be slotted to accept a screwdriver. If not slotted, screws may be removed with pliers.

4. Bases of some percolators have gaskets between the base and the body that should be examined. If damaged, the gasket should be discarded and replaced with a new one. However, if the unit is an immersible percolator, treat the percolator as non-immersible once the base has been removed on the chance that the sealing qualities are destroyed. Nonimmersible means that the unit's base should not be submerged in water when the percolator is being washed.

Replacing the thermostat (18)

1. Remove the base (24) as just described.

2. Disconnect the two leads at the thermostat (18).

3. Using a pair of needle-nose pliers, gently raise up on the top part of the thermostat's hold-down spring (not shown).

4. Slip the thermostat to the side, so the end of the spring slides through the groove in the thermostat.

5. Install a new thermostat by tipping the part so you can engage the groove in the thermostat with the hold-down spring.

Possible difference: Some units have the thermostat and leads riveted together. To disconnect the leads from the thermostat, you must grind off the rivet heads using a small hand grinder or file and tap out the rivet with a punch. You should use steel Pop rivets to reassemble leads to the thermostat.

Replacing pilot light, heating element and lead assembly

1. Remove the base (24).

2. Disconnect the pilot light, heating element and lead assembly (17) from the terminal pins (20) and thermostat (18).

3. Using the wiring diagram shown in the main illustration, reconnect a new pilot light, heating element and lead assembly (17) to the thermostat (18) and terminal pins (20).

Possible differences:

1. Some percolators don't have pilot lights.

2. Heating elements of some percolators are molded into the base, and the base has to be replaced to replace the element.

3. Heating elements and pilot lights of other units may be replaced individually.

Vacuum cleaner repair

■ A VACUUM CLEANER is a simple appliance; with the aid of trouble-shooting charts on the following pages, you should be able to deal with most of its common problems. The machine is basically a motor-driven fan with a nozzle attached, either directly or with a hose, to its low-pressure end. Atmospheric pressure forces air into the nozzle and dirt is carried with it and on through into the bag.

There are two types: the upright and the tank or canister. The upright usually, and the tank sometimes, has a motor-driven brush to loosen embedded dirt.

Nearly all vacuum cleaners use universal motors with replaceable carbon brushes. These bear under spring pressure on the commutator; they are eventually consumed and when worn, can cause problems. Many vacuum-cleaner designs offer direct access to brushes.

You can test the suction of a hose-equipped cleaner with a vacuum gauge, available through most heating and refrigeration-supply houses; it simply plugs into the hose. Vacuum is expressed in terms of water lift—how many inches above its normal level a column of water is pulled—and between 50 and 70 in. is normal for most cleaners.

When motor armature and fan both turn freely, a malfunctioning vacuum cleaner's trouble is probably electrical. Tests are outlined on the next page. If the ohmmeter reading for the entire circuit is higher than 2-4 ohms, it may indicate poor connections; no reading (infinite resistance) may indicate an open or shorted circuit. You can also check the circuit for grounds by placing one lead of the ohmmeter or continuity tester on one plug prong and the other on any *metal* part of the cleaner, then doing the same with the other prong. There should be no readings. Most cleaners have one or more capacitors across the circuit to eliminate radio interference; if a short or ground is indicated, remove the capacitor and retest. If the short or ground disappears, replace the capacitor with one of exactly the same value.

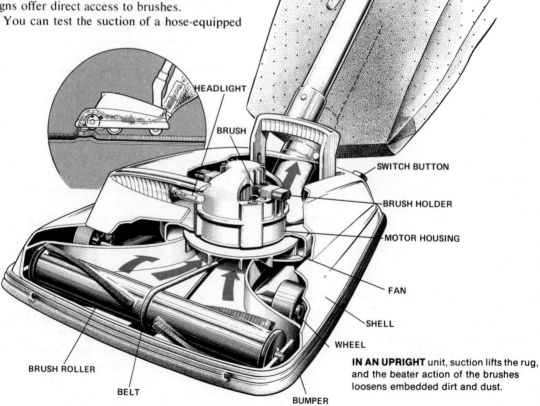

HEADLIGHT

BRUSH

SWITCH BUTTON

BRUSH HOLDER

MOTOR HOUSING

FAN

SHELL

WHEEL

BRUSH ROLLER

BELT

BUMPER

IN AN UPRIGHT unit, suction lifts the rug, and the beater action of the brushes loosens embedded dirt and dust.

Motor will not run

POSSIBLE CAUSES	WHAT TO TRY
1. Fuse blown or circuit breaker tripped.	Replace fuse or reset circuit breaker. If blowing or tripping is repeated, disconnect power and check for shorts.
2. Line cord defective.	Inspect cord for breaks or fraying. Check for continuity by removing cord at terminals; placing one lead of tester on plug prong, other on corresponding terminal wire, flex cord. There should be an uninterrupted reading. Repeat for other prong, wire. Replace cord if there is no reading or flexing cord interrupts reading.
3. Switch defective.	Place continuity-tester leads on switch terminals; turn switch on. There should be a reading. Turn switch off. There should be no reading. Replace switch if there is variation.
4. Connection loose at terminal block.	Check all terminal-block connections; tighten any found loose.
5. Motor brushes worn or sticking.	Check lengths of brushes. Replace them if ¼ in. or shorter. Check for free brush movement in holder. If tight, sand brushes just enough to make them slide easily.
6. Armature shorted or open.	Place ohmmeter test leads on brush holders, rotate armature manually. Resistance reading should remain fairly constant. Sharp decrease indicates short, infinite reading indicates open. Replace armature in either case; new motor may be required.
7. Fan jammed.	Check for obstructions, clear. Replace fan if bent or damaged.
8. Motor bearings frozen.	Disassemble motor, clean and lubricate bearings. Replace bearings if worn.
9. Motor defective.	Disconnect both motor leads; direct test with 110-v. jumpers. Replace motor if defective.

Straight-suction upright

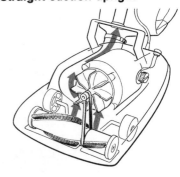

Typical brush assembly

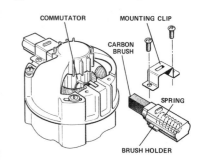

COMMUTATOR   MOUNTING CLIP
CARBON BRUSH
SPRING
BRUSH HOLDER

Motor stops and starts

POSSIBLE CAUSES	WHAT TO TRY
1. Intermittent break in line cord.	Shake cord while vacuum is running; inspect for wear. Test continuity as explained above.
2. Loose connection.	Check entire circuit; tighten all connections.
3. Switch defective.	Test switch as explained above.
4. Wiring shorted.	Locate short, repair, insulate with electrical tape.

Motor runs too slowly

POSSIBLE CAUSES	WHAT TO TRY
1. Bearings tight or misaligned.	Disassemble motor; check, realign and lubricate bearings. Replace bearings if worn.
2. Fan jammed.	See chart, "Motor will not run" (above).
3. Brush contact poor.	Check brush length as in chart, "Motor will not run." If length is okay, stretch brush springs slightly.

Typical tank-type cleaner

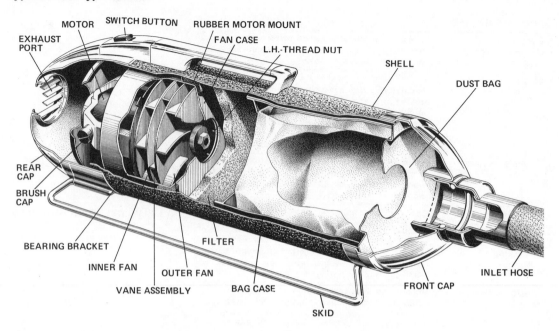

EXHAUST PORT · MOTOR · SWITCH BUTTON · RUBBER MOTOR MOUNT · FAN CASE · L.H.-THREAD NUT · SHELL · DUST BAG · REAR CAP · BRUSH CAP · BEARING BRACKET · INNER FAN · OUTER FAN · VANE ASSEMBLY · FILTER · BAG CASE · SKID · FRONT CAP · INLET HOSE

Motor runs too fast

POSSIBLE CAUSES	WHAT TO TRY
1. Fan loose.	Check and tighten fan.
2. Armature shorted.	See chart, "Motor will not run."
3. Dust bag overloaded.	Replace or clean bag.

Motor sparks

POSSIBLE CAUSES	WHAT TO TRY
1. Commutator dirty.	Clean thoroughly with trichlorethylene, sand with 2/0 or finer sandcloth.
2. Brushes worn.	See chart, "Motor will not run."
3. Brushes new.	Normal. Sparking will diminish when new brushes wear to shape of armature.
4. Armature wire open.	See chart, "Motor will not run."

Motor is noisy

POSSIBLE CAUSES	WHAT TO TRY
1. Foreign matter.	Clean out motor.
2. Brushes new.	Normal. Noise will diminish when new brushes wear.
3. Armature obstructed.	Check armature bearings for misalignment or wear; realign or replace.
4. Fan bent or loose.	Check fan, tighten on shaft. Replace fan if blades are bent.

Suction is weak

POSSIBLE CAUSES	WHAT TO TRY
1. Attachment or hose connection loose.	Check hose, attachments to make sure connections are tight.
2. Obstruction in hose or attachment.	Check for large pieces of paper, pins, wads of lint, and clear.
3. Cover loose.	Check for correct insertion of bag. Adjust and reclose cover.
4. Bag overloaded.	Replace or clean bag.
5. Hose leaking.	Check entire length of hose for cracks, holes. Replace hose if any are found. Also check for tight connections between hose, tank and attachments.
6. Exhaust port clogged.	Clear exhaust port.
7. Belt broken.	(Upright models.) Replace belt.
8. Agitator brush jammed.	(Upright models.) Clear brush of all foreign matter—brush should turn freely.
9. Nozzle setting wrong.	Check nozzle setting according to manufacturer's instructions for type of cleaning being done.

Dust leaks into room

POSSIBLE CAUSES	WHAT TO TRY
1. Holes in dust bag.	Replace bag.
2. Bag installed incorrectly.	Check manufacturer's instructions for correct installation of bag.
3. Sealing gasket defective or leaking.	Check gasket, replace if worn or broken. Also check gasket alignment where cleaner opens for insertion and removal of bag.
4. Bag overloaded.	Replace or clean bag.

Electrical tests

Place test leads across: 1. A and G to test entire circuit (should be 2-4 ohms); 2. A and B, G and H to test line cord (there should be continuity in each leg); 3. C and D to test switch; 4. E and F, I and J to test field coils (there should be continuity in each); 5. I or E and motor case to test for shorts (there should be no continuity); 6. F and J to test armature, turning it by hand (resistance reading should be constant). Tests 1 and 6 require ohmmeter; rest can be done with continuity tester. Power must be disconnected for *all* tests.

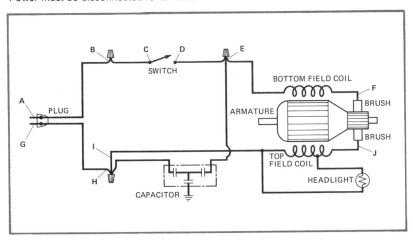

Canister variations

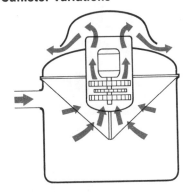

TOP-MOUNTED MOTOR (SHOP VACUUMS)

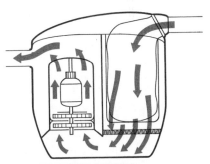

SIDE-MOUNTED MOTOR

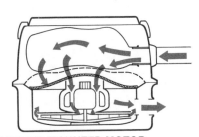

BOTTOM-MOUNTED MOTOR

AIR CUSHION

Pop-up toaster repair

■ THE POP-UP TOASTER is not an appliance that is easily repaired if it suffers a major parts failure. How it operates is not difficult to comprehend, but in practice the various mechanisms, levers, elements and switches make this one of the most difficult appliances in the home to salvage if a major breakdown occurs (Figure 1).

Fortunately, there are redeeming factors. First of all, the electric pop-up toaster is probably the most reliable small appliance you own. It probably will last a score of years or more, and the cost of a replacement is not great. Furthermore, if it does develop a malfunction within a relatively short period of time, the cause more often than not is a *minor* one that is easy to fix.

Keep things in perspective. Do not probe for complex answers to simple problems.

How electric pop-ups work

An electric pop-up toaster must perform several distinct functions in order to give you your morning toast. It must latch the cradle (carriage) holding bread firmly in place when the lever controlling the cradle is pushed down. It must then turn on electricity so the heating elements that do the actual toasting can begin glowing.

As with room heaters, the heating elements in a toaster are commonly made of a nickel-chromium alloy, called nichrome. Elements are connected in parallel in most toasters, so they are controlled by a common conductor.

Smaller toasters have three elements so two slices of bread may be toasted simultaneously. Larger toasters have more than three elements so that four or more slices of bread can be handled at a time.

Caution: A toaster's heating elements are not insulated. Touching one, even if the toaster is not turned on, may result in serious injury since one side of the heater circuit is always "live"—it is in constant touch with the wall outlet. When working on a toaster, make certain that it is disconnected from the wall plug except when taking voltage readings. In this case, keep the toaster disconnected until the voltmeter is connected—then plug it into the outlet, but keep your hands away from "live" elements.

Another function that an automatic toaster must perform is to shut off the current to the elements when the toast is done. At the same time it must trigger a latch that allows the cradle to surface. However, the spring-loaded cradle must have a brake on it to prevent it from snapping up too forcefully, which could cause the toast to fly halfway across the room. (Indeed that happened frequently in the very early models!)

Manufacturers have devised various methods to perform each of these functions. There is no reason to delve into each method that has been used—there are too many. A general discussion of the more common methods probably will cover your model (Figure 2).

Generally speaking, when you push down the cradle-control lever, you cause the cradle to engage a mechanical latch. (In models in which bread lowers itself automatically, a motor is used. When bread is placed in the cradle, it causes a switch to close that starts the motor which lowers the rack by means of gears.)

At the same time that the cradle is lowered, a switch is closed that activates the heater-element circuit, allowing current to flow and elements to glow.

"Light," "medium," or "dark" toast commonly is achieved by a timing mechanism that winds itself up when the cradle is pushed down. A bimetal regulator (or compensator) is used in many toasters so the first slices of toast, which are made with a cold appliance, will be toasted

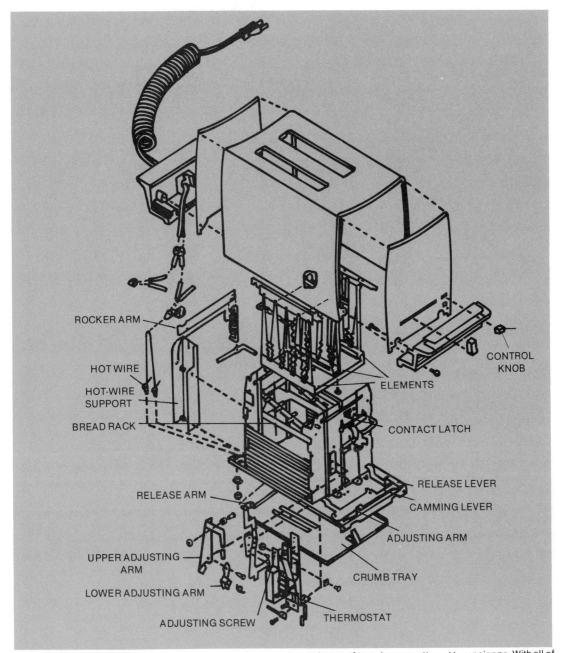

ROCKER ARM

HOT WIRE

HOT-WIRE SUPPORT

BREAD RACK

ELEMENTS

CONTROL KNOB

CONTACT LATCH

RELEASE ARM

RELEASE LEVER

CAMMING LEVER

ADJUSTING ARM

UPPER ADJUSTING ARM

LOWER ADJUSTING ARM

CRUMB TRAY

ADJUSTING SCREW

THERMOSTAT

FIGURE 1. This drawing of a typical electric pop-up toaster shows what you face when you attempt to repair one. With all of its mechanisms, it is one of the most intricate small appliances.

the same as the second and subsequent slices, which are made with a hot appliance.

When the toaster is cold, the bimetal regulator is straight and does not come into contact with the timing mechanism. The mechanism is allowed to wind down for the longest period of time, giving bread more time to toast.

However, with the toaster hot and subsequent slices of bread placed in it for toasting, less time is needed. Heat affects the bimetal strip, bending it toward a speed-control lever. This lever controls the timing mechanism. When the lever is "pushed" by the bimetal strip, it causes the mechanism to speed up, which in turn results in a shorter period of operation of the timer.

The timing mechanism is set for light or dark toast, or any degree in between, by turning a knob or sliding a lever on the outside of the case.

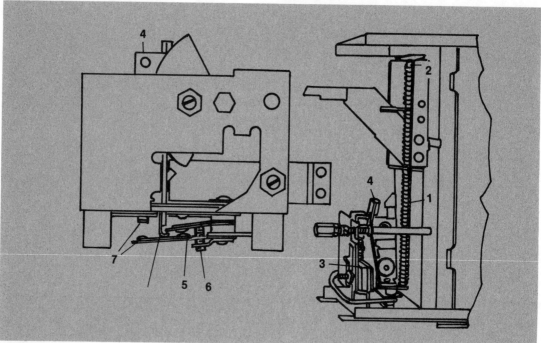

FIGURE 2. Thermostatically controlled cradle mechanism includes: (1) rack-return spring; (2) guide rod; (3) latch mechanism; (4) metal blade; (5) contact points; (6) hooking mechanism; (7) contact points; (8) adjustment mechanism.

Actually, all you are doing is setting the position of the speed-control lever.

When the timer runs down, an auxiliary switch is forced open. It turns off the electricity going to the heating elements, allowing the elements to start a cool-down. At the same time, some kind of mechanism activates and trips the latching mechanism, allowing the cradle, which is spring-loaded, to pop up.

One type of latch release is called a hot-wire release, because it consists of a strand of wire that connects to the line voltage and is attached to the latch. As current flows through it, this wire gets hot and expands. But when current to the elements is shut off, it is also shut off to the hot-wire release. The wire cools down and contracts. As it contracts, it "pulls" the latch release with it, thus releasing the cradle.

Another interesting element in an electric pop-up toaster is a shock absorber, or snubber, that cushions the cradle as it springs up. This device is similar in operation to a pneumatic stop that is employed by storm doors to keep the door from slamming. The snubber puts the brake to the cradle, allowing it to ease up so the toast doesn't fly out.

The big foes: crumbs and crud

Most problems with an electric pop-up toaster are caused by food particles. Crumbs can affect both the mechanical and electrical operation of the unit.

For example, bread crumbs which drop inside the appliance can hamper the cradle latch, preventing the cradle from holding in a down position. This, of course, keeps the toaster from operating. In addition, contact points of switches can become coated with food matter, such as raisins. This can prevent electrical connections and thus toaster operation.

You should clean your toaster periodically and thereby avoid foreign-matter problems.

Most toasters have clean-out traps that permit you to reach inside and brush out dirt (Figure 3). First *detach the power cord*. Open the trap door and brush particles from all surfaces you can reach with a one-inch paint brush that is used only for this purpose (Figure 4).

If the toaster doesn't have a trap door, disconnect the power cord and turn the appliance upside down. Shake it vigorously (Figure 5).

If the unit develops a problem and has to be disassembled, make certain that you clean the

FIGURE 3. From time to time, open the trap of toaster and let loose crumbs fall out.

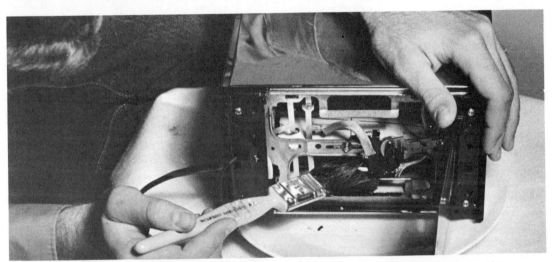

FIGURE 4. The insides of the toaster are delicate, so use a 1-inch paint brush to dislodge stubborn crumbs.

FIGURE 5. If the toaster doesn't have a clean-out trap, turn the unit upside down and shake it.

FIGURE 6. You can use compressed air to get rid of crumbs that the paint brush can't reach.

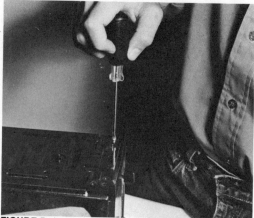

FIGURE 7. In disassembling a pop-up toaster, first remove all exposed screws.

parts as thoroughly as you can. It's still possible that crumbs, raisins, or jelly are the cause of the trouble.

The best "tool" to clean toaster parts is compressed air. You can employ it even if you don't have a compressor and air hose (Figure 6).

Visit a photography shop. Most such shops sell compressed air in a can with a nozzle. Photographers use it for cleaning dust from negatives. It is ideal for cleaning out the inside of a toaster.

When you are inside a toaster, examine all contacts and other parts carefully for burned matter which compressed air won't remove. This will have to be scraped off—carefully.

Take pains to make sure that the scraper doesn't slip accidentally and rupture a heating element.

After cleaning mechanical parts—springs, levers, catches and so forth—lubricate them lightly with a heat-resistant grease. This is available from hardware stores, but make sure that the tube stipulates that the lubricant may be used on toasters and other heat-generating appliances.

Caution: Do not apply lubricant to electrical components.

When crumbs aren't the cause

Essentially there are five problems that can afflict an electric pop-up toaster. They are:
1. The toaster doesn't work at all.
2. The toaster burns the toast.
3. The toast doesn't pop up.
4. The toast is either too light or too dark.
5. The bread doesn't toast evenly.

The easiest repairs, strangely enough, are made if the toaster doesn't work at all, assuming

that all elements don't suddenly burn out at once, which isn't likely to happen. Start, of course, by examining the power cord.

Next, to check the innards, make sure that the power cord is pulled from the wall outlet. Remove the light-dark control knob, which is usually only pressed into place (Figures 7, 8, 9).

Now look for a set screw holding the cradle-control lever in place. Remove it and the lever. Unscrew all the screws you can find holding the cover and whatever ornamental trim must come off so the cover can be lifted, revealing the inside of the toaster.

The first thing to do is to give everything a very close look. See if you can spot loose connections or broken wires. Make sure the toaster end of the line cord is okay and is held tightly by its terminals.

Now check voltage, using a voltmeter on both sides of the main switch. Replace a switch if there is a lack of voltage. Other than line-cord problems, a bad switch is the chief reason a toaster will refuse to function.

Important: To check voltage, you must depress the cradle to close the switch. Don't forget to connect the power cord to a wall outlet. *Be careful!*

Suppose your problem is uneven toast, which is a common thing. Chances are that one element is burned out or a wire has come loose, disconnecting the element from its conductor. You can buy a new heating element in many cases, but before you do, check the cost of repair against the cost of a new toaster. This should be done in every instance where a repair is a major one.

The best way to discover and correct the most common causes of electric pop-up toaster problems is to use the chart on the next page.

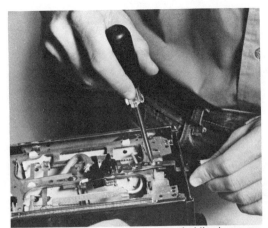

FIGURE 8. Second, remove all screws holding levers, so they don't block disassembly.

FIGURE 9. With screws out, internal mechanism can be removed from the shell.

TROUBLE	USUAL CAUSES	HOW TO CORRECT
Toast is either too dark or too light	• Timer setting incorrect	• Check position of timer control knob or lever.
	• Timer mechanism has gone awry	• Replace
Bread doesn't toast evenly	• Heating element is open	• Check for loose connections; replace element if necessary.
	• Reflective surfaces are dirty	• Clean
Toaster doesn't work at all	• Damaged power cord	• Replace
	• Open switch	• Replace
	• Impediment between latch and catch	• Clean away foreign deposits and make sure tension of clutch is sufficient to make effective contact.
Toast burns	• Improper timer setting	• Check position of timer control knob or lever.
	• Bimetal regulator is distorted	• Replace
	• Auxiliary (cool-down) switch stuck closed	• Replace
Cradle doesn't pop up	• Bread, raisins or some other foreign matter impeding catch release	• Clean thoroughly and lubricate.
	• Bimetal regulator is distorted	• Replace
	• Hot-wire or some other catch release mechanism damaged or burned out	• Replace
	• Cradle spring broken or lacks tension	• Replace

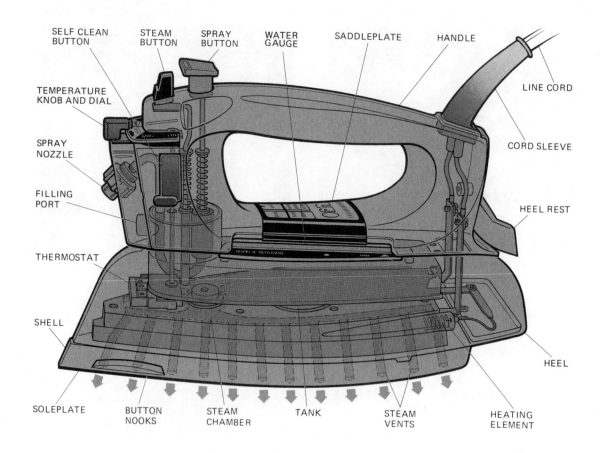

SELF CLEAN BUTTON · STEAM BUTTON · SPRAY BUTTON · WATER GAUGE · SADDLEPLATE · HANDLE · LINE CORD · TEMPERATURE KNOB AND DIAL · CORD SLEEVE · SPRAY NOZZLE · FILLING PORT · THERMOSTAT · HEEL REST · SHELL · HEEL · SOLEPLATE · BUTTON NOOKS · STEAM CHAMBER · TANK · STEAM VENTS · HEATING ELEMENT

Iron repair

■ ELECTRICALLY, AN IRON is simple; its electrical circuit consists of cord, thermostat and heating element. Iron thermostats are of two types: bimetal and base-expansion. In the first, a bimetal strip makes and breaks contacts as temperature changes. In the second, a thin metal strip welded to the base of the thermostat falls and rises to make and break contacts as the base contracts and expands with temperature changes.

In either type of iron thermostat, the spring tension on thermostat elements is varied to give different temperature, settings, and the iron, once hot, will cycle on and off within a few degrees of the desired temperature. Thermostat contact points may become pitted or corroded in time, and if an iron is dropped, insulators and bimetals may break.

It is usually better to replace a thermostat than to repair it. Thermostat calibration requires an iron tester; one may be worthwhile only if you plan to check a number of irons.

Heating elements are chrome-nickel resistance wire, either a replaceable ribbon element wound on a sheet of mica, or a round wire element in a ceramic form cast into the iron's soleplate. The cast-in type is expensive to replace when found defective; you're better off buying a new iron than trying to replace such an element. Heating-element failures are opens (breaks),

Iron does not heat

POSSIBLE CAUSES	WHAT TO TRY
1. Blown fuse or tripped circuit breaker.	Replace line fuse or reset circuit breaker. If blowing or tripping is repeated, check iron for shorts.
2. Defective cord or plug.	Inspect cord and plug for fraying or breaks. Disconnect cord from outlet and iron and test each wire for continuity. If either gives no reading, replace with cord of correct size.
3. Loose connections at iron terminals.	Tighten both connections at eyelet terminals on iron.
4. Loose thermostat-control knob.	Replace knob and tighten on shaft.
5. Defective thermostat.	Disassemble iron for access to thermostat. Replace thermostat if parts are broken.
6. Defective heating element.	Test element for continuity. If there is no reading, replace removable element; discard iron with cast-in element.

Iron produces too little heat

POSSIBLE CAUSES	WHAT TO TRY
1. Low voltage.	Test voltage at wall outlet with voltmeter. If not within 10 percent of normal, call local power company.
2. Thermostat out of calibration	Recalibrate iron only with an iron test stand. Set text for information on source.
3. Defective thermostat.	See preceding chart.
4. Loose connections at terminals.	See preceding chart.

Iron produces too much heat

POSSIBLE CAUSES	WHAT TO TRY
1. Thermostat out of calibration.	See preceding chart.
2. Defective thermostat.	See chart, "Iron does not heat" (top above).

CAUTION: Be sure power is turned *off* before you handle components. Make all continuity tests with power *off*. Use your manufacturer's manual to locate components, and use only replacement parts that meet his specifications.

DRY IRON

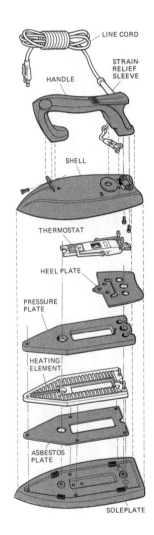

LINE CORD
STRAIN-RELIEF SLEEVE
HANDLE
SHELL
THERMOSTAT
HEEL PLATE
PRESSURE PLATE
HEATING ELEMENT
ASBESTOS PLATE
SOLEPLATE

grounds and shorts. A shorted element will usually blow itself apart when it is turned on, in turn blowing the line fuse; afterward it will test as open.

Steam irons operate two ways: with a tank that also serves as a boiler or, in the flash type, with valving that drips water into a steam chamber—a recess in the hot soleplate—where it vaporizes. A spray feature adds a pump to the hardware. Hard water is the enemy of steam irons, as it leaves mineral deposits that build up and clog valves and ports. Distilled water is recommended in its place.

When a steam-iron problem involves inaccessible parts, disassembly should be done with caution because of the complexity of valves and linkages. Get the manufacturer's service instructions, and take the iron apart only as far as necessary to gain access to the faulty component.

BOILER-TYPE STEAM IRON

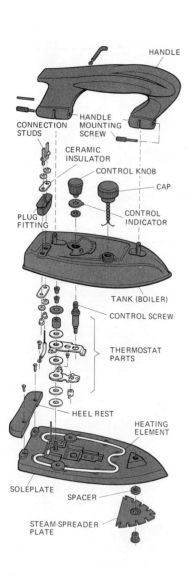

HANDLE
CONNECTION STUDS
HANDLE MOUNTING SCREW
CERAMIC INSULATOR
CONTROL KNOB
CAP
PLUG FITTING
CONTROL INDICATOR
TANK (BOILER)
CONTROL SCREW
THERMOSTAT PARTS
HEEL REST
HEATING ELEMENT
SOLEPLATE
SPACER
STEAM-SPREADER PLATE

Water leaks from iron

POSSIBLE CAUSES	WHAT TO TRY
1. Tank overfilled.	Do not fill tank completely. Water expands when heated.
2. Defective seam or tank weld.	Disassemble iron for access to tank, replace tank, reassemble iron.
3. Damaged tank gasket.	Disassemble iron for access to gasket, replace gasket, reassemble iron.

Iron does not steam

POSSIBLE CAUSES	WHAT TO TRY
1. Tank nearly empty.	Refill tank.
2. Thermostat set low or out of calibration	Set thermostat higher or recalibrate if necessary. See chart, "Iron produces too little heat."
3. Valve OFF.	Turn valve to ON position.
4. Clogged valves or steam ports.	Clean iron by filling its tank with vinegar and turning it on.

Iron spits

POSSIBLE CAUSES	WHAT TO TRY
1. Wrong setting of thermostat.	Set thermostat higher. Spitting usually is caused by low thermostat setting.
2. Internal mineral deposits.	Clean iron with vinegar as described in preceding chart.
3. Tank overfilled.	Do not fill tank completely.

Spray does not work

POSSIBLE CAUSE	WHAT TO TRY
1. Defective plunger or assembly.	Disassemble iron for access to plunger and the plunger assembly. Replace any worn or broken parts.

Iron stains clothes

POSSIBLE CAUSES	WHAT TO TRY
1. Starch on soleplate.	Clean soleplate with damp cloth, buff with steel wool and polish with dry cloth.
2. Minerals in water.	Use distilled water in iron.
3. Sediment in tank.	Clean with vinegar. See chart, "Iron does not steam."

Iron tears or snags clothes

POSSIBLE CAUSE	WHAT TO TRY
1. Rough, spot, nick or burr on soleplate.	Buff soleplate with fine emery, polish with dry cloth.

Iron gives shocks

POSSIBLE CAUSES	WHAT TO TRY
1. Defective cord.	Check cord for frays, cracks, exposed bare wires. Replace with cord of correct size for iron.
2. Thermostat insulation break.	Disassemble iron to get at thermostat; look for broken porcelain or asbestos. Replace assembly.
3. Heating element grounded.	Test for ground with one lead of continuity tester on element, other on iron chassis. A reading indicates a ground. Replace removable element; discard iron with cast-in element.

Iron sticks to clothes

POSSIBLE CAUSES	WHAT TO TRY
1. Dirty soleplate.	Clean soleplate. See chart, "Iron stains clothes."
2. Excess starch in clothing.	Reduce amount of starch used and lower temperature setting.
3. Temperature roo high for fabric.	Lower temperature setting. Consult manufacturer's instructions on fabric type involved.

FLASH-TYPE STEAM IRON

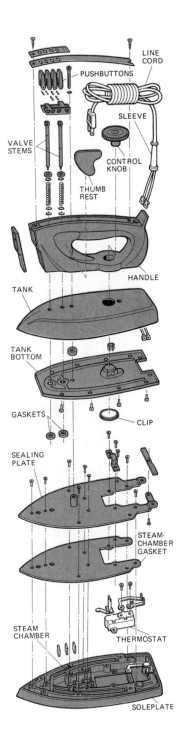

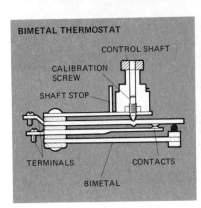

BIMETAL THERMOSTAT

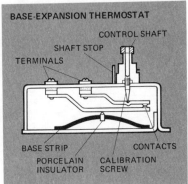

BASE-EXPANSION THERMOSTAT

Food mixer repair

■ MOST electric food mixers are powered by motors of the universal type with carbon brushes. This type of motor develops high torque and speed, but is noisy and, because the brushes tend to spark, requires capacitors to prevent radio and TV interference. To deal with foods of different consistencies, the motor must turn at different speeds. The three common methods of speed control are a centrifugal switch, tapped field and adjustable brushes.

The centrifugal switch is a governor that keeps the motor at the desired speed by shutting off and restoring current. When the motor is off, its contacts touch. The contacts stay together until the motor reaches a speed at which centrifugal force overcomes spring tension and the contacts separate, breaking the circuit. The motor then slows until the spring can bring the contacts together again. The cycle is short enough that the motor

TYPICAL MIXER COMPONENTS

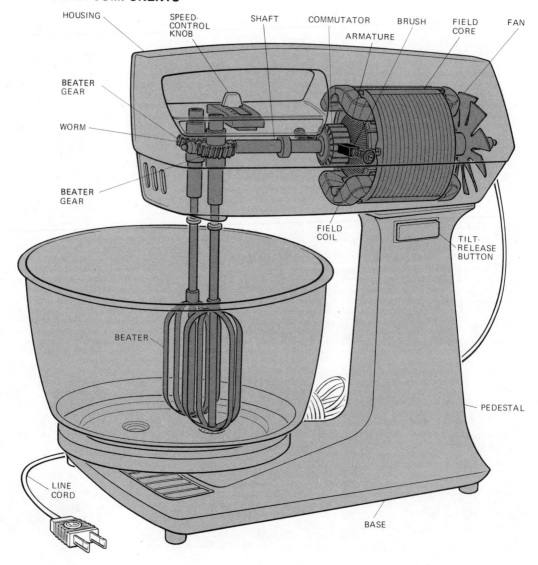

HOUSING
SPEED-CONTROL KNOB
SHAFT
COMMUTATOR
ARMATURE
BRUSH
FIELD CORE
FAN
BEATER GEAR
WORM
BEATER GEAR
FIELD COIL
TILT-RELEASE BUTTON
BEATER
PEDESTAL
LINE CORD
BASE

runs smoothly. Speeds are varied by moving the adjustable contact.

With tapped-field control, parts of the field coil are cut out of the motor circuit, giving it lower resistance and producing higher speed. At low speed, the entire coil is used. A medium setting, using part of the tapped coil, provides moderate speed.

PEDESTAL MIXER: GEARBOX

Motor does not run

POSSIBLE CAUSES	WHAT TO TRY
1. No power.	Check for power at wall outlet with 115-v. test lamp. If there is no reading, replace line fuse or reset circuit breaker.
2. Defective cord.	Disconnect cord from outlet and then from motor casing. Test wires in cord for continuity. If either gives no reading, replace cord.
3. Worn brushes.	Remove brush caps from mixer housing. Pull out carbon brushes. If they have worn down to ¼ in. or less, replace them.
4. Defective on-off switch.	Remove switch and inspect contacts for pits or burned spots. Clean contacts with a fine file or sandpaper (do not use emery cloth). Test for continuity across terminals. If there is no reading with switch on, replace it.
5. Open field coil.	Test coil for continuity with one probe at wire junction of the cord, capacitor and field lead, other at lead from coil. There should be a reading. Also test between other coil lead and lead to brushes. There should be a reading. If there are no readings, replace field coil or check price of a new mixer.
6. Open armature winding.	Test for continuity across each segment of the commutator. Replace armature if any segment gives no reading. Test for armature short by placing one probe on commutator segment and the other on armature body. Replace armature if there is a reading.
7. Centrifugal switch stuck open.	Press switch closed. Clean all moving parts of the switch and put a drop of oil on the pivot point—do not over-oil.

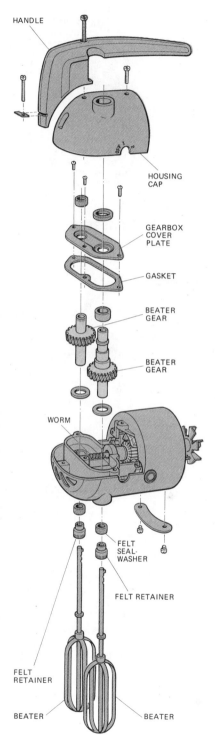

HANDLE

HOUSING CAP

GEARBOX COVER PLATE

GASKET

BEATER GEAR

BEATER GEAR

WORM

FELT SEAL-WASHER

FELT RETAINER

FELT RETAINER

BEATER

BEATER

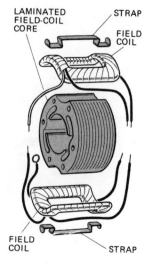

LAMINATED FIELD-COIL CORE · STRAP · FIELD COIL · FIELD COIL · STRAP

FIELD ASSEMBLY

Motor does not run, blows fuses

POSSIBLE CAUSES	WHAT TO TRY
1. Jammed bearings or spindles.	Remove gear housing. Apply penetrating oil to spindles; remove them at setscrews. Clean gear case, spindle holes with trichloroethylene solvent. Replace worn, broken gears. Grease gear compartment with proper lubricant, reassemble.
2. Jammed armature.	Disassemble mixer. Straighten or replace armature shaft. Spin armature by hand to check for clearance. Reassemble mixer.
3. Shorted line capacitor.	Test capacitor for continuity. There should be a reading for a split second. If no reading or if it is permanent, replace the capacitor.
4. Defective field coil or armature.	See preceding chart.
5. Shorted line cord.	Remove cord from outlet and then from motor casing. Test for continuity across plug prongs. If there is a reading, replace the cord.

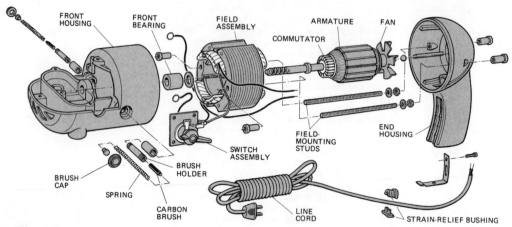

FRONT HOUSING · FRONT BEARING · FIELD ASSEMBLY · COMMUTATOR · ARMATURE · FAN · FIELD-MOUNTING STUDS · END HOUSING · SWITCH ASSEMBLY · BRUSH HOLDER · BRUSH CAP · SPRING · CARBON BRUSH · LINE CORD · STRAIN-RELIEF BUSHING

MOTOR ASSEMBLY

TYPICAL BRUSH ASSEMBLY

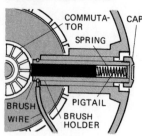

COMMUTA-TOR · CAP · SPRING · BRUSH WIRE · PIGTAIL · BRUSH HOLDER

Motor overheats

POSSIBLE CAUSES	WHAT TO TRY
1. Centrifugal switch stuck closed.	Remove switch, separate contacts by hand. Check contacts for pits or burned spots. Clean with fine file or sandpaper (not emery cloth). Put a drop of oil on pivot point—do not over-oil.
2. Motor dirty.	Clean motor air intake with vacuum cleaner. Remove stubborn dirt with small toothbrush. Do not use solvents on internal motor parts.
3. Field coil or armature shorted or grounded.	Look for burn marks near edges of commutator segments, indicating a shorted or grounded winding. Test for continuity between commutator segment and shaft; a reading indicates a short or ground. Test field coil with one probe on coil lead, other on mixer housing. Replace any parts that produce readings.

Motor speed erratic

POSSIBLE CAUSES	WHAT TO TRY
1. Defective cord.	Test each side of cord for continuity while wiggling cord. Any variation in reading indicates a break. Replace cord.
2. Worn brushes.	See chart, "Motor does not run."
3. Loose connections.	Check all solder joints and wiring insulation. Correct any defects found.
4. Defective motor speed control.	See chart, "Motor overheats." Check tapped field by testing for continuity across resistor. Replace resistor if there is no reading. Test motor capacitor; see chart, "Motor does not run, blows fuses." Check adjustable-brush control by examining brushes; see chart, "Motor does not run."

TAPPED—FIELD SPEED CONTROL

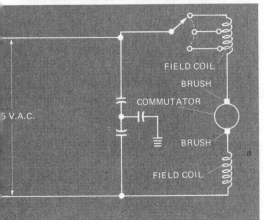

ADJUSTABLE—BRUSH SPEED CONTROL

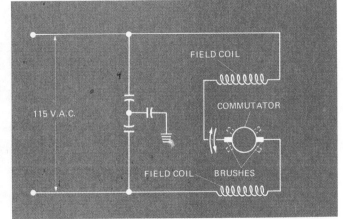

Noisy operation

POSSIBLE CAUSES	WHAT TO TRY
1. Worn bearings.	Tighten or replace bearings.
2. Play at end of rotor.	Shim rotor end with small thrust washers, .005 to .025 in. thick.
3. Motor dirty.	See chart, "Motor overheats."
4. Gears broken or dry.	Remove gear housing, check for chipped or broken gear teeth or lack of lubricant. Replace all worn or broken gears and grease with the recommended lubricant.
5. Bent beaters.	Straighten beaters so they clear each other.
6. Bent fan blades.	Straighten fan blades to clear housing.

CENTRIFUGAL—SWITCH CONTROL

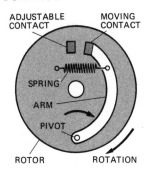

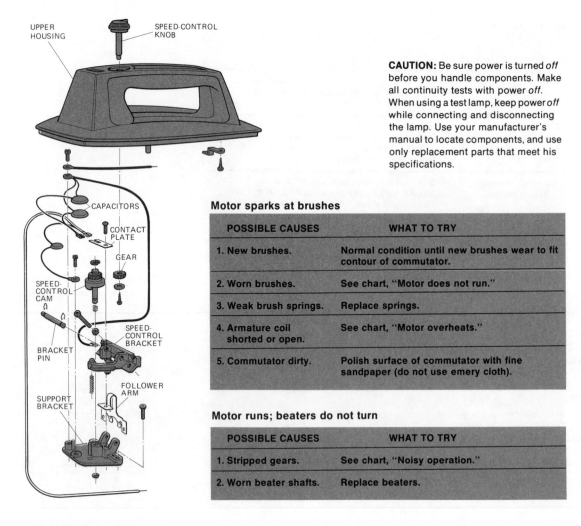

CAUTION: Be sure power is turned *off* before you handle components. Make all continuity tests with power *off*. When using a test lamp, keep power *off* while connecting and disconnecting the lamp. Use your manufacturer's manual to locate components, and use only replacement parts that meet his specifications.

Motor sparks at brushes

POSSIBLE CAUSES	WHAT TO TRY
1. New brushes.	Normal condition until new brushes wear to fit contour of commutator.
2. Worn brushes.	See chart, "Motor does not run."
3. Weak brush springs.	Replace springs.
4. Armature coil shorted or open.	See chart, "Motor overheats."
5. Commutator dirty.	Polish surface of commutator with fine sandpaper (do not use emery cloth).

Motor runs; beaters do not turn

POSSIBLE CAUSES	WHAT TO TRY
1. Stripped gears.	See chart, "Noisy operation."
2. Worn beater shafts.	Replace beaters.

**HAND-MIXER: UPPER
SECTION AND CONTROLS**

MOTOR ASSEMBLY

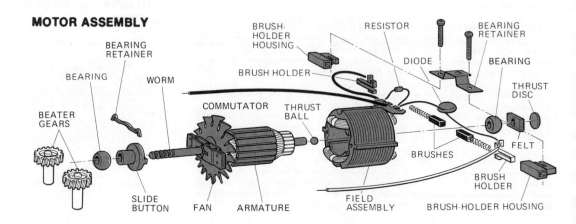

Motor runs slowly or lacks torque

POSSIBLE CAUSES	WHAT TO TRY
1. Wrong speed for load.	Change speed.
2. Load too heavy.	Not mixer's fault; don't use on unusually stiff mixtures.
3. Worn brushes.	See chart, "Motor does not run."
4. Rotor binding.	Check for proper end-play clearance—this clearance should be .005 in.
5. Centrifugal switch stuck closed.	See chart, "Motor overheats."
6. Field coil grounded to mixer housing.	Place one probe of 115-v. test lamp on mixer housing, other probe on known ground. If there is a reading, replace field coil or check price of a new mixer.

Motor runs continuously

POSSIBLE CAUSES	WHAT TO TRY
1. Switch dial broken.	Cam pin broken or worked loose. Replace.
2. On-off switch shorted.	Test for continuity across switch terminals with switch off. Replace switch if there is a reading.

Adjustable-brush control provides lower motor speeds by moving the brushes away from their position of maximum efficiency with respect to the commutator. This type of control reduces torque as it reduces speed, and for this reason is not commonly found on new machines.

At one time or another, a food mixer will require lubrication for proper performance. Some mixers have accessible oil holes or grease cups that permit lubrication without disassembly. If water or another liquid has found its way into the gearbox, all of the old grease should be removed and the compartment repacked with grease of a weight recommended by the manufacturer of the mixer.

Many mixer problems can be solved without taking the appliance apart. Stuck beaters can be loosened by squirting penetrating oil into their sleeves. Bent beater blades can be straightened, although a bent beater shaft usually requires replacement. If beaters slip in their spindles, the trouble is usually a worn shaft that should be replaced. Brushes are accessible through caps on the mixer housing. When you must take a mixer apart, keep careful track of the sequence of disassembly so that you can reverse the process with a minimum of difficulty.

LOWER SECTION AND GEARBOX

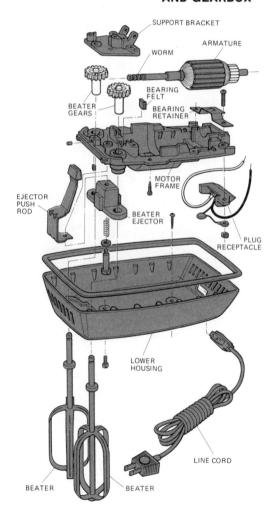

Portable food mixer repair

■ REPAIRING a hand-held mixer isn't exactly a cinch. However, you may be surprised at how easy it can be.

Disassembling the mixer

1. Withdraw the screws (1) holding the case (2).

If screws are inserted through the top of the case, they are often placed beneath an escutcheon plate which may be removed by prying with a screwdriver after removing a retaining screw(s). Some escutcheon plates aren't held by screws, but are pressed into place.

2. After removing screws, carefully lift off the case.

3. Remove the ejector knob (4) and switch assembly (7), held by a speed nut (5).

4. Unhook the ejector spring (6) and ejector plate (8).

5. Lift the ejector plate to disconnect it from the switch assembly. You may have to manipulate the switch so the ejector plate slips up past the switch knob. You may also have to force the ejector plate against the field coils (9 and 10) to slip the plate from its slot in the switch bracket.

Important: As you perform this step, carefully notice the way it's done. Reassembly is performed in reverse order.

6. Withdraw the screws (11)—in this model there are four—holding front and rear bearing straps (12 and 13), switch assembly, thrustplate retainer (14) and thrust plate (15). Remove these parts.

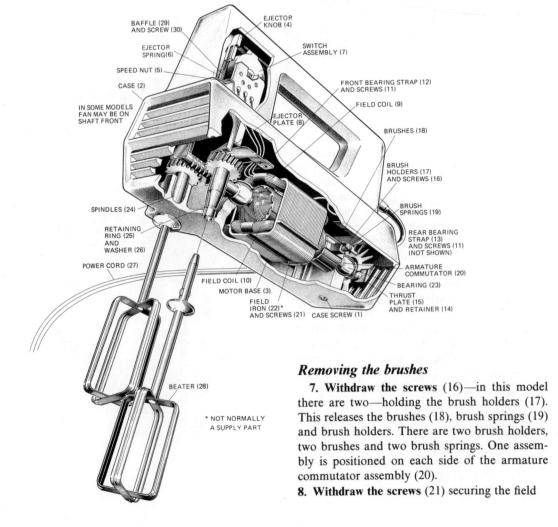

BAFFLE (29) AND SCREW (30)
EJECTOR KNOB (4)
EJECTOR SPRING (6)
SWITCH ASSEMBLY (7)
SPEED NUT (5)
CASE (2)
FRONT BEARING STRAP (12) AND SCREWS (11)
FIELD COIL (9)
IN SOME MODELS FAN MAY BE ON SHAFT FRONT
EJECTOR PLATE (8)
BRUSHES (18)
BRUSH HOLDERS (17) AND SCREWS (16)
SPINDLES (24)
BRUSH SPRINGS (19)
RETAINING RING (25) AND WASHER (26)
REAR BEARING STRAP (13) AND SCREWS (11) (NOT SHOWN)
POWER CORD (27)
ARMATURE COMMUTATOR (20)
FIELD COIL (10)
MOTOR BASE (3)
FIELD IRON (22)* AND SCREWS (21)
CASE SCREW (1)
BEARING (23)
THRUST PLATE (15) AND RETAINER (14)
BEATER (28)
* NOT NORMALLY A SUPPLY PART

Removing the brushes

7. Withdraw the screws (16)—in this model there are two—holding the brush holders (17). This releases the brushes (18), brush springs (19) and brush holders. There are two brush holders, two brushes and two brush springs. One assembly is positioned on each side of the armature commutator assembly (20).

8. Withdraw the screws (21) securing the field

Motor won't run

POSSIBLE CAUSES	WHAT TO TRY
1. No voltage at the receptacle.	Check with a table lamp.
2. Damaged or defective power cord.	Inspect and/or test for continuity.
3. Bad switch.	Replace.
4. Other electrical breakdowns.	Check the circuit for continuity. If no open condition shows up, conduct checks outlined for a motor which has insufficient speed or power.

Motor has insufficient speed or power

POSSIBLE CAUSES	WHAT TO TRY
1. Bearing or spindle is binding.	Tap appliance in the vicinity of the front and rear bearing straps and field iron with a small hammer or the handle of a screwdriver as the motor is running. An increase in speed indicates a binding condition.
2. Brushes are worn.	Inspect.
3. Shorted armature.	Check armature resistance from segment to segment on the commutator. Field resistance is about 5 ohms and commutator resistance, bar to bar, should be about 3 ohms. If resistance is noticeably lower or higher, replace the armature.

Motor speed cannot be adjusted

POSSIBLE CAUSES	WHAT TO TRY
1. Bad switch.	Replace.
2. Shorted capacitor.	In those units that use a capacitor, replace.

Motor is noisy

POSSIBLE CAUSES	WHAT TO TRY
1. Dry spindles	Lubricate.
2. Worn spindles	Replace.
3. Worn bearing	Replace.
4. Bent fan	Replace fan, if possible—replace armature if fan is an integral part.
5. Defective armature	Replace.

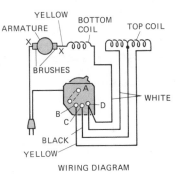

WIRING DIAGRAM

iron (22) to the case. Here there are three screws.

9. You can now remove the armature and replace the bearing (23) on the commutator end if necessary.

10. Remove spindles (24) by spreading the retaining rings (25). Slide the rings and washers (26) off spindle shafts, and lift spindles out of the top of the motor base.

11. If the power cord (27) has to be replaced, melt soldered joints. In all cases of electrical repair, make sure solder joints are made properly. Use the wiring schematic here as a guide in making electrical repairs, such as replacing the switch, field coils or power cord.

Replacing beaters

12. Beaters (28) should be examined if the appliance runs but beaters don't revolve, spin sluggishly or whip. Look for bent rods and wear on beater tips. Replace them in pairs.

13. The baffle (29) may be replaced, if damaged, by removing the baffle screw (30).

Reassembling a portable food mixer is done the reverse of disassembly. Spindle shafts should be lubricated with appliance gear grease before they are put back in the motor base.

Food processor repair

■ REPAIRING A FOOD PROCESSOR is as easy as whipping egg whites in one.

Since replacement parts are somewhat hard to get, it would be a good idea to call your dealer to see if parts for your machine are available. If they aren't, you may be able to substitute a "universal" part. Disassemble the unit, find the defective part and take it to a store that's listed in the classified directory under "Electric Appliances—Small—Supplies, Parts."

Units are similar inside

There isn't much difference between units when it comes to troubleshooting and repair. However, there is one notable difference between some units: Most use a cogged belt and two pulleys to drive the shaft, but some use a gear train.

Except for this, internal mechanisms are much the same from unit to unit. Parts include a universal motor; a rectifier (diode) that converts incoming a.c. to d.c., which is needed to run the motor; on-off and safety switches; and a power cord. These are the parts that cause problems.

Two common problems

There are only two major problems that occur with any degree of frequency:

1. The motor won't run although the on-off switch is "on" and the bowl and bowl cover are locked in place. Locking the bowl and bowl cover in place trips the safety switch to "on."

2. The motor runs, but the shaft and blades won't turn.

Motor won't run

The causes are the following:

- No power
- Defective power cord
- Defective on-off switch
- Defective safety switch
- Defective rectifier
- Defective motor

Caution: Observe safety practices when troubleshooting and repairing. For example, don't leave a blade or disc attached.

Start by plugging the processor into another outlet in a different part of the house. If the motor starts running then your problem is with a defective house line—not with the unit.

Check the power cord for damage:

Unplug the unit and check the power cord for damage.

Remove the assembly screws from the underside of the bottom housing and separate the top and bottom housings. Don't force them apart. If they still hold tightly together, look for hidden screws—for example, under a nomenclature plate which you may have to pry off.

Check all connections for any that may have come loose. Also look for burned insulation on wire leads. Replace defective leads.

When you test the *on-off switch,* the power cord has to be plugged in with the safety switch engaged. When you test the *safety switch,* the power cord has to be plugged in and the on-off switch has to be "on." Test these switches by carefully using a jumper wire to bridge the switch terminals (or remove the switch leads and temporarily tape them together). If the processor comes to life in either case, replace the switch involved.

At this point, only a small rectifier and motor remain as causes for failure. Replace the rectifier. It isn't expensive. With luck, the motor will run now. If not, you probably need a new motor.

Shaft won't turn

A bent shaft could cause this malfunction, but a bent shaft is not a common occurrence. It is more likely that the belt has broken or one of the pulleys has stripped. If your food processor uses a gear-driven shaft, one of the gears probably has stripped. The solution, in any case, is to find the defective part and replace it.

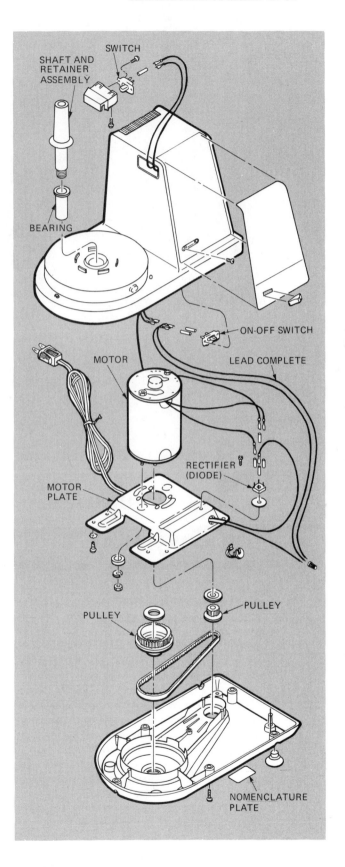

Snow removal the easy way

■ WITH EACH PASSING YEAR, for many of us, the snow seems to be getting heavier. A long driveway can seem almost endless after a heavy snowfall.

You can make a snowplow at a minimal cost and only about four hours' work with hand tools. Since it weighs only about 90 lbs., you can build it in a basement and then drag it up the stairs. It will not do everything a more expensive commercial unit will do—you have to get out to lift the blade after each run. And it will ride on top of hard ice or frozen snow, rather than scrape it. But that's a small inconvenience for the price difference.

Design yours to suit your vehicle. The plow can be scaled down for use on a family car equipped with studded snow tires or chains.

PLOW IS attached to the vehicle by chains wrapped around bumper, then hooked over the projecting nailhead.

A primary consideration is providing the means for attaching a chain (or mounting); a sturdy luggage rack, trunk opening, trunk handle, or—on the front end—a loop of heavy wire fastened to the radiator support and arranged to project when the hood is closed. The suspended weight is only 65 lbs., so the selection is more convenience than engineering.

Make a full-size sketch of the side of the plow, showing your bumper cross section the proper distance from the ground. Lay out the plow face and the angle of the frame and draw the bumper notch, remembering that the plow must have good bearing on your bumper when down, and must not bind when you lift it. Leave heavy stock below the bumper, and use a separate frame cap to support the raised bumper end of the frame.

Lay out the frames and saw them. Space the frames to suit your bumper supports, trailer hitch, or any place that will take the thrust. Nail the vertical ribs to the 2x8s of the plow face, letting the ribs project ⅝ in. below the lower 2x8 to back up the 1x4 shoe. Then nail the frames to the proper ribs, leaving enough space below the frames for the lower stiffener. It is notched to provide good bearing against the ribs to which they are nailed as well as to the frames. A 2x4 is cut to fit between the frames at their bumper end and nailed in place, using two small nails to avoid splitting. Cut and fit the diagonal braces and nail them in place. The upper stiffener rests on the frames and is notched to fit the diagonals.

The joint where the frames, crosspiece, and diagonals meet is nailed sparingly (to prevent splitting the lumber). For reinforcing, force a heavy wire through drilled holes, wedge and twist it tight, and nail down the sharp ends.

Consider the shoe as expendable. In a rough driveway, expect it to last one or two seasons at the most. Make it from any inexpensive wood. You can use a length of 1x4 furring and bevel it to ride over broken concrete. If your drive has a smooth tie-in with the street, you can probably leave the edge square.

A heavy dog chain provides the attachment and lift chains. Decide where the attaching chain can pass around your bumper and provide some lateral control. The lift chain is 3 ft. long and has a heavy ring at one end and a hook at the other.

The plow shown has moved hundreds of pounds of loose, broken-up ice and plowed through 2-ft.-high snowdrifts.

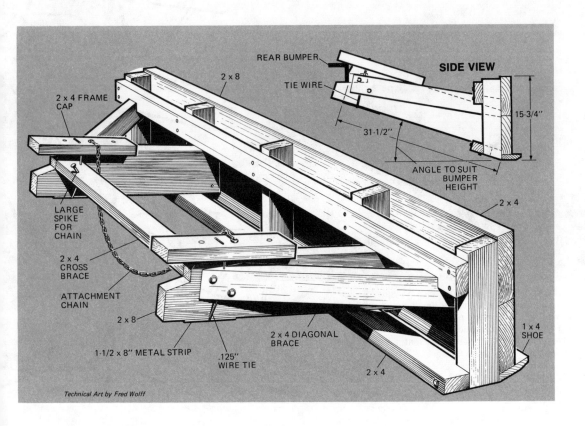

Technical Art by Fred Wolff

Snow-melting systems you can install

■ HOW MANY TIMES have you grumbled to yourself about there "being a better way" as you headed outdoors, shovel in hand, to clean the walks? There *is* a better way. Snow-melting systems can be installed to keep ice and snow from accumulating on your roof and to clear your driveways and sidewalks.

Three types of snow-melting systems are available for home use: 1. Electric heating cable can be installed on your roof to eliminate snow dams on the overhang. 2. An electric heating cable system can be embedded in driveways and sidewalks. 3. A hydronic pipe system in which a heated mixture of antifreeze solution or hot oil circulates through the pipes to melt the snow can also be embedded in the pavement.

Heating cables can help prevent damage to the roof gutters and interior walls of your home. They melt the snow, eliminating heavy snow and ice accumulation on roof overhangs and stopping ice dams from forming in gutters and downspouts.

Ice and snow accumulations tend to develop particularly on homes with large roof overhangs

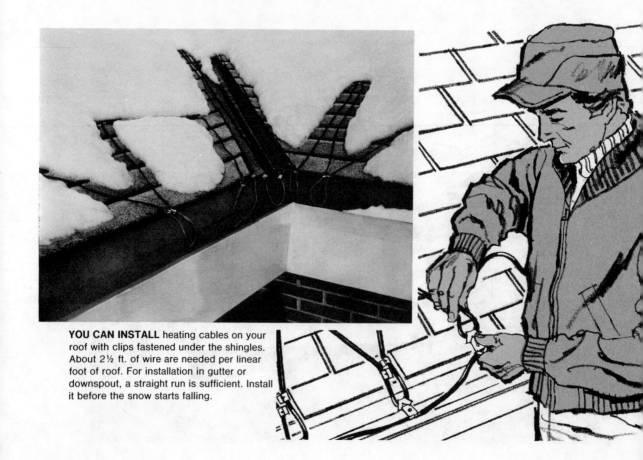

YOU CAN INSTALL heating cables on your roof with clips fastened under the shingles. About 2½ ft. of wire are needed per linear foot of roof. For installation in gutter or downspout, a straight run is sufficient. Install it before the snow starts falling.

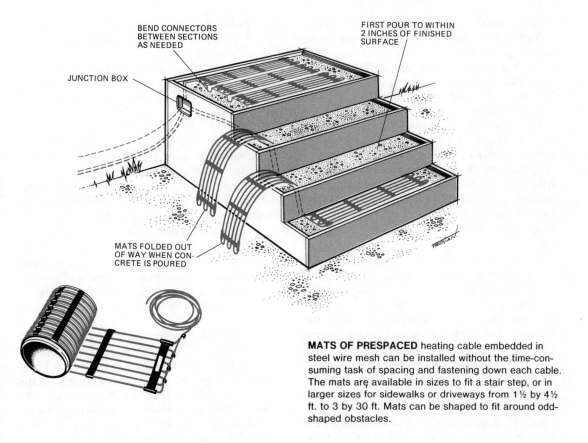

BEND CONNECTORS
BETWEEN SECTIONS
AS NEEDED

FIRST POUR TO WITHIN
2 INCHES OF FINISHED
SURFACE

JUNCTION BOX

MATS FOLDED OUT
OF WAY WHEN CON-
CRETE IS POURED

MATS OF PRESPACED heating cable embedded in steel wire mesh can be installed without the time-consuming task of spacing and fastening down each cable. The mats are available in sizes to fit a stair step, or in larger sizes for sidewalks or driveways from 1½ by 4½ ft. to 3 by 30 ft. Mats can be shaped to fit around odd-shaped obstacles.

that are not warmed by heat from the building interior. Snow dams are formed when sunshine and heat rising from the heated building partially melt ice and snow on the upper part of the roof. The slush runs down to the old gutter or unheated roof overhang where it again turns to ice and continues to collect. Beneath this buildup, water rises under the shingle tabs, spills over the back shingle edges and can drain through the layers of stapled felt paper, down the rafters, and onto interior ceilings and walls.

The cable that prevents these ice dams is an insulated wire that heats to melt the snow when electrical current flows through it. It is available in varying lengths from 5 to over 160 feet. The cable and kits that include clips for fastening it to the shingles are available at hardware stores and electrical supply houses. Each length of cable is equipped with a cold lead wire, several feet long. It plugs into a waterproof outlet box, usually located near the eave. The cable operates on normal house current of 120 volts and consumes electricity at a rate of 6 to 16 watts per foot.

You should install the cable in a zigzag pattern along the roof edge. In this pattern about 2½ feet of wire are needed per linear foot of roof. For installation in gutter and downspout a straight run of wire is used. Where eaves don't overhang the house, you may only need cable in the gutter and downspout to melt the snow. If heating cables are used on either roof overhang or gutter, the downspout must also be heated to carry away the water from the melted snow and ice. A heated length of wire is dropped inside the downspout to the bottom (even if it is underground), using weights if necessary. All gutters and downspouts should be grounded to a driven ground rod.

The best way to provide electric current to the cable is to locate waterproof outlets on the exterior walls of your home fed by a No. 12 gauge or other heavy wire. Cables can't be shortened or spliced. Each length must be plugged in separately.

To turn on the system easily, a switch should be located inside the house. A pilot light that shines when the system is on is recommended to remind you to turn off the system when it's not needed.

Heating cables in pavement

Melting snow and ice on driveways and sidewalks is easily done by means of heating cables embedded in the cement or asphalt. These cables are available either already prespaced in mats, or in individual lengths which can be laid down at spaced intervals.

Mats can be cut to follow contours or to curve around objects. However, care must be taken that the heater wire is not damaged.

Cables are covered with plastic insulation which permits them to be buried directly into concrete or asphalt. Cold lead wires are attached to the heating cable. These lead wires must be long enough to reach a dry location for terminating.

Snow-melting systems are designed for average conditions. This means that during heavy downfalls the snow will accumulate slightly. You can minimize installation and operation cost by using two 18-inch-wide heat strips for the wheel tracks of your car, rather than a system to melt snow off the entire driveway.

You can install heating mats and lay individual cable yourself. A licensed electrician can wire and connect the units to the household electric supply. A reputable supplier of heating equipment can usually give adequate advice on the capacity needed for your situation and the method of connection. Manufacturers can also give helpful information.

The spacing of individual heating cables depends on the watts-per-square-foot required, which varies with the average number of hours and inches of snowfall per year in each area. Cable is usually rated at 10 watts per square foot.

When you install the cable, a lead wire must terminate at a junction box. The junction boxes can be placed in the slab where the cable is laid, or brought out to a main supply point. If boxes are exposed to weather they must be of the outdoor waterproof type as specified by the National Electric Code.

Wires can be laid when new cement or asphalt drives are built. To wire an existing asphalt drive, a cable-asphalt sandwich can be built.

Hot fluid melting systems

An alternative to the electric cable method of melting snow from driveways and sidewalks, particularly for large homes and commerical use, is the hydronic pipe snow-melting system. Pipes are embedded in the pavement through which heated anti-freeze or oil circulates to melt snow.

A standard system uses ¾-inch pipe on 12-inch centers buried within concrete, or on 9-inch centers in asphalt. These pipes are in S-shaped coils that can be connected by means of a supply and return main to a heat exchanger which is attached to the house heating boiler or auxiliary boiler.

Components needed for the system include a gas or oil-fired boiler, heat exchanger, heater pump, expansion tank, gauges, valves and controls, the pipe that circulates the liquid and the liquid. A boiler needed to melt snow on a 500-square-foot area would take up less space than a washing machine in your basement. Flexible polyolefin and rigid copper tube or wrought-iron pipes are among those used in the system. A thermostat is also suggested for heat control.

Some manufacturers provide a package arrangement including design, engineering, materials, labor, on-site inspection and a guarantee for installing the system. This package is the most trouble-free but also the most expensive. A homeowner who is handy could purchase needed materials and do his own installation for much less. However, it would be wise to employ a specialist for welding work if rigid pipe is used.

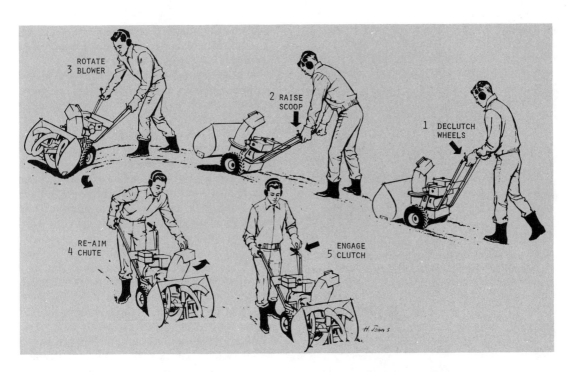

Snowblowers: tips to make the job faster

■ THE TACTICS of farm or street plowing just don't work when you're clearing your property with a snowblower. You have to consider many more things.

First is the snow-removal area itself—a conventional walk, side drive close by the house, two-car garage ramp or a long, exposed drive are typical. Other factors are:

Type of surface. A smooth, hard surface is easiest; just set the blower height low. Crushed rock and gravel take a higher setting; rocks and pebbles thrown far and wide create a safety hazard.

Grades, slopes. A level-running speed may suddenly become too fast for a steep downgrade. A runaway snowblower pursued by a frantic householder isn't funny.

Targets to avoid. A neighbor's picture window, windshield, children and dogs are vulnerable to hard-flung stones or ice.

Property or machine damage. Stones along flowerbeds, buried survey stakes, shrubs, flowers and ditches should be cased and marked before starting. It's easy to tear up both blower and obstacle.

Wind direction. If you have a smooth, more-or-less even depth of snow, try starting the cut so the wind will cross your path at an angle, thus blowing snow to right or left. If a building is a factor, make a first cut close to it and cast the snow away.

Two mistakes often beset the beginner. First, television ads show blowers throwing snow 40 ft. or more, with the chute discharge high. This rooster tail may be impressive, but it's seldom necessary or practical. Sooner or later it will lash back and leave you gasping. There's a chance that the blower will pick up something you didn't know was there and fling it into a target you don't want to hit.

The second mistake is assuming that unless the snow is thrown far away it will be handled a second time, doubling the work. A few trials

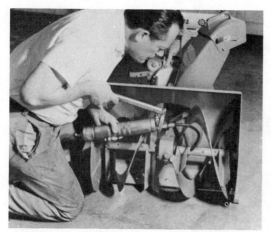

CHECK OWNER'S MANUAL for lube points. This unit was accidentally delivered with a dry, auger gearbox.

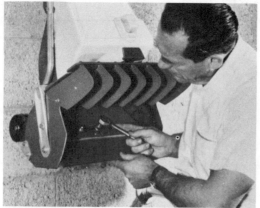

PLASTIC PADDLES on lightweight blower are easily replaced. Be sure to check for the proper clearance.

with the chute aimed down will convince you this isn't true. Chewed-up snow redeposited in an uncleaned area just isn't a problem.

Another tactical error is based on the farmer's plowing method. You may feel that the most efficient approach is to make a constant circle or loop pattern.

It's better to make a pass close to your starting point, reverse the blower and back up for another pass; then repeat until you have a cleaned area that allows a nice easy turnaround and realignment for the next cut. Some time is lost in backing, but the cleaned area lets you reverse and turn the chute at the same time without throwing snow over the cleaned portion.

Sometimes this forward-and-reverse method is best for the whole job—especially on a bitterly cold day with a high wind. Just turn your back to the wind and keep it there. Generally, however, it's practical to do this for three or four passes at each end of your work area.

With room to turn at each end you just start a series of loop passes at the windward side and work towards the downwind finish point.

Learning how to turn a blower around properly takes practice. One good method is to declutch the hand clutch just as you come to the end of the loop. This disconnects the power from the drive wheels. At the same time, bear down on the hand grips and elevate the scoop a few inches so the auger doesn't start picking up snow until you're headed into your new pass.

Always turn so your body goes into any side or quartering wind. Turning the other way places

WOODEN SHIMS give adequate adjustment when the blower is to be used on a smooth, even surface.

SPRAY WAX applied to the inside of chute and discharge area will prevent snow from sticking to the metal.

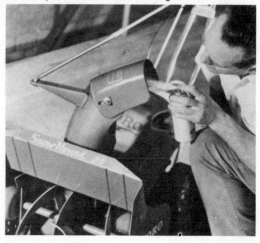

the chute discharge between you and the wind.

On a straight walk or drive, usually you start to the windward and work to the lee with up-and-down passes. If working quarters are tight, such as a driveway between two houses, it is often practical to discharge the snow into a central windrow by working from both sides. This narrow heap of snow can then be cleaned up by starting at the garage and working toward the street with chute discharging straight ahead. A street plow throws it on your drive, so you might as well throw some back.

Hardened drifts, always tough to clear, are formed by heavy snow and howling winds. Often they are preceded by rain so that lower layers are soaked and well glued to the surface. When followed by below-zero weather, the drifts become almost solid and lower snow layers are rock hard. The usual snow blower doesn't have the weight and ripping power of a commercial plow to get under this type of drift. Instead, it rides up over the drift and trims a little off the top. A number of techniques can help:

• Remove the little skids on the snow scoop to get the sharp scoop edge down into the snow as much as possible.

• Place a sack of sand or salt on the scoop to hold it down.

• Put chains on blower drive wheels.

• As the auger bites into the hard, deep snow, declutch drive wheels so the blower can digest and clear the material. This lets all the engine power feed the blower and doesn't crowd the machine faster than it can work. By clutching and declutching with a rhythmic pattern, the blower will dig in and back off in a series of bucking actions, like the rocking of a stuck car.

• Break up the worst areas with a shovel jammed downward at intervals or use a small paddle-type blower to chop up the hard spots, then clear with the big machine. Amazingly, these lightweights will tear into snow the big augers can't touch. Small machines, gas or electric-powered, can be scooted all over like a vacuum cleaner or picked up in a two-hand grip like a shovel. They will clean steps and tough spots easily.

Regard the paddles as expendable. Made of a tough, durable plastic, they will take all sorts of arm-jarring beatings and come up smiling. Replace them after the season to be ready for next year.

If you don't already have a snowblower, check the kind of snow-removal problem you have before you buy. No blower is ideal for all jobs. Often a small paddle-wheel type and a larger auger model may do the work faster and easier than a single blower. Here are other considerations:

Slopes and grades. Dragging a heavy blower back uphill is dangerous. If you have a slope, be sure to buy a machine with power reverse. If the area is small, a superlight job without reverse is good.

Steps, porches and patios. A big auger job is practically useless for cleaning small areas or a series of steps. A light gas or electric paddle-wheeler can be handled like a shovel.

LOW DISCHARGE is less dramatic than high rooster tail, but it is a more practical setting for the chute.

LIGHTWEIGHT paddle-type blower is best for steps and small areas. It can also break up large drifts.

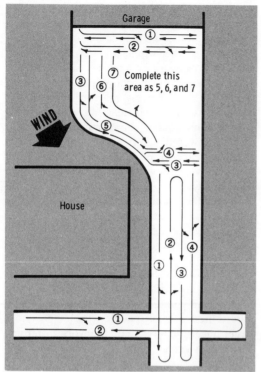

WIND DIRECTION is one of the most important factors to consider when planning your attack. Here are two methods of handling a more-or-less typical layout that demonstrate how the pattern is varied to suit the wind.

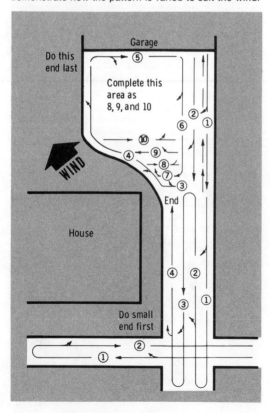

Long runs. Clearing long drives and walks can get tedious, especially when snow cover is moderate, unless the blower has three or four forward speeds. A good one travels at a peppy walk. Fixed-speed types will merely prolong your exposure.

Storage. If you can wheel the blower into a garage or shed, size and weight are no problem. If you'll store it in a basement or elevated porch, think light.

Special uses. Maybe you want to take your blower to a hunting cabin or carry it in your car's trunk in case you get stuck.

Snowblower design and construction is not quite so standardized as that of automobiles. With a new blower, give yourself an hour of unhurried study to read the instructions and examine the guts of your machine. Search out the lubrication points, and if you don't have the grease guns, oil cans and lubricants, spend a bit to set up for quick servicing during the heavy-use season. Time spent now and an occasional lubrication and chain and belt adjustment will save hours of future trouble.

Before you take your new blower out for a trial spin, keep these points in mind:

Panic stop. Know the quickest and safest way to cut the engine in case you should run into an unexpected obstacle.

Blower declutch. With a dog-clutch drive to the blower you can tear things up by trying to engage a dead blower shaft with a spinning, main-drive shaft. Your instructions will give the proper sequence. You can also play hob with your blower by driving it into a garage or storage shed with the auger spinning.

Fuel shutoff. Some engines have none; others have a manual shutoff valve and a few have carburetor drains that dump a trickle of gas when stopping. Leaking gas in a closed, heated garage can spell danger. If you have a gas valve, get in the habit of closing it.

When spring finally arrives, take an hour or so to prepare your snow blower for summer:

• Get rid of all old gas in tank and carburetor. Run it dry, if necessary.

• Drain the oil; replace it with fresh.

• Grease and oil all bearings, chains.

• Replace the vee belts if they look worn.

• Replace the sparkplug.

• Oil the control linkages and Bowden wire cables.

Finally, if it was a hard season, have your repair agency look over the clutch and drive train before next fall's rush.

Solar energy guide

■ IN MANY supposedly primitive societies, homes were built to take maximum advantage of the warmth of sunlight and the coolness of the night. Until recently, this common-sense approach to energy use was all but forgotten in the modern world where fuel seemed abundant and limitless.

But things changed. As we discovered that fuel was not quite as abundant as we supposed or as cheap as we had come to expect, we also found good reason to use nature's own thermostat.

The most obvious sign of this increased awareness is the number of solar collectors popping up on the roofs of all types of buildings in all parts of the country. The sight of solar collectors and photovoltaic cells will be no more unusual than the ever-present television antenna.

Two solar systems

Solar energy breaks down into two broad categories: active and passive. Passive solar systems use energy from the sun much as earlier societies did in their structures—by getting maximum use of the sun as it strikes a building. Passive measures include the positioning of the building on the site, materials used, design, insulation and placement of glazing.

Active solar systems, on the other hand, are the ones we usually think of when we hear the term "solar energy." They use hardware to convert and transport heat. But an active solar system does not work to capacity without support from passive techniques as well.

Site selection

Site orientation is important. The long sides of the building should face north and south, with most of the glass toward the south. In most parts of the country, the prevailing winds are from the west, hence a shorter west wall cuts infiltration

from those wintry blasts. Even more important is the effect of the sun. The west wall also picks up the greatest heat gain in the summer, so the reduction of this area has benefits the year round.

During the winter, the sun travels from east to west low in the southern sky. Windows facing south tend to act as passive solar collectors, picking up a great deal of the sun's heat.

If the same building is to be air-conditioned, the summer sun angle is extremely high so you can exclude it from those windows with overhangs. With an active system, a long south wall has the added advantage of presenting a large roof area properly oriented for solar collectors.

Active systems

These systems are used to provide domestic hot water and space heating. Given the rising costs of fossil fuel, solar domestic water and space heating is now cost-effective in many parts of the country. But solar-powered air-conditioning is still too expensive to be practical.

Most active solar systems in homes or large commercial buildings have four basic elements:
● They use a collecting device to gather the heat from sunlight.
● They have a storage system to accumulate the heat for nighttime and cloudy-day use.
● They have a delivery system to bring the heat to the spaces to be conditioned.
● They have a backup system for days when there is not enough sunlight or stored heat to do the job.

The solar collector

The purpose of a collector is to gather sunlight (radiant energy) and convert it to heat (thermal energy). Either air or liquid is circulated through a collector to pick up the heat and carry it to its destination.

There are three general types: flat plate, evacuated tube and concentrating collector. The last two are used primarily for high-temperature systems that can include airconditioning. Flat-plate collectors are by far the most common type used, both for residential domestic hot-water and space-heating installations.

The heart of a flat-plate collector is an absorber plate made of metal (copper, aluminum, stainless steel) which has tubing that is either bonded to it or an integral part of it. Heat transfer fluid passes through this tubing. The plate is enclosed in a sealed frame and is painted flat black or covered with a material that retains heat. The back of the absorber plate rests against a layer of insulation. An air space over the surface

faces the sun, covered by one or two layers of glazing (glass or a type of plastic).

Collectors should be oriented to the south, but the fall-off in performance as you vary from due south is not that great. You can vary the collectors' angle from 20° east to 45° west of due south with only a 6 or 7-percent drop in performance, a feature that opens up many design options.

Although a good flat-plate collector can get up to 200° F. for residential space heating and domestic hot-water systems, there is no reason to go above about 140° F. While it would seem the higher the temperature the better the performance of the solar system, in the case of flat-plate collectors the reverse is true.

Keep it cool

Heating systems are designed to use the lowest temperature they reasonably can, since flat-plate collectors operate more efficiently at lower temperatures.

The higher the temperature of the collector, the greater the temperature difference between collector and outside air. A big temperature difference means more heat lost to the outside air. Yet the greater the heat loss to the outside air, the slower the transfer fluid must flow through the collector to absorb the same amount of heat.

Freeze protection

When liquid is used, it is generally either water or an antifreeze solution. With water, the danger of freeze-ups exists in most parts of the country, and some drain-down technique must be built into the system to prevent freeze damage to the collectors. Many systems are designed to drain automatically when the circulating pump shuts off.

The antifreeze alternative presents its own problems. First a heat exchanger must be incorporated into the system to transfer heat from the antifreeze circulating through the collectors to the large water storage tank most frequently used. Due to the high cost of antifreeze, it is economically prohibitive to fill the storage tank (about 1000 gallons for a residential space-heating system) with this liquid. But a heat exchanger reduces the efficiency of the system because some energy is lost in the transfer process.

Another problem is that many antifreeze solutions are toxic and some parts of the country have codes (for good reason) against using toxic substances on the heat supply side and potable water on the hot water supply side of single solar water systems. Also, be it water or antifreeze, liquid collectors can develop leaks.

A lot of hot air

Air collectors, on the other hand, tend to be simpler and less risky, with a lower initial cost.

On the negative side, air is not as good a heat transfer medium as water. As a result, the collectors are slightly less efficient, and so is the storage. While in most water systems the heat is stored in water, in most air systems rocks are commonly used for heat storage.

Unfortunately, stone has about one-fifth the heat storage capacity per pound as does water. Thus, three to five times more space is needed for air-system heat storage than for liquid. Stones used must be thoroughly cleaned and air going to the collectors must be filtered.

Distribution systems

The most basic active solar system is a domestic water heater piped to a set of collectors. But the heater should include a conventional heating mechanism to supplement the solar system.

The next step up the ladder includes solar space heating. The most direct way is to route solar-heated water from a collector array through a coil placed in the return air duct of a conventionally fired furnace. Or, in the case of an air system, warm air can be introduced directly from the collectors into the return air duct. Either way, a standard furnace blower distributes heat throughout the building.

Fan coil units are used in larger buildings where individual room temperature control is desirable. Here, the hot water is piped directly to the rooms to be heated. Each room has a fan which blows air over a set of coils through which hot water passes.

Combined systems

In most solar space-heating installations, a domestic water heating device is also included. In some cases, a heat exchanger leading from the conventional domestic hot water tank is immersed in the solar water storage tank. In others, the heat exchanger is immersed directly in the domestic hot water tank.

With air systems, the heat exchanger is placed in the path of the hot air coming off the collectors. Sometimes, the hot-water tank itself is used as a heat exchanger and buried in the rock storage pile to absorb heat directly from it.

Combined systems can reasonably be expected to provide 50 to 60 percent of space heat and 80 to 85 percent of hot water for a family living in a typical single-family house.

The major portion of cost is tied up in collectors. The number of collectors needed depends on the home's location, construction and size. But as a rule of thumb you can figure that for space heating and hot water the amount of collector needed will equal one-third to one-half the floor space of your home. A 2000-square-foot home could, therefore, require some 700 square feet of collectors.

Technically, it is feasible to provide 100 percent of all heating needs with solar energy, but in most parts of the country the amount of collector area and storage needed for such a system would not be practical. Therefore, a backup system is almost always used, the most common being a forced-air furnace. Becoming increasingly popular is the heat pump.

Heat-pump assistance

Heat pumps are not only making themselves felt in the solar field; they're coming into their own as conventional heating-cooling devices.

Basically, a heat pump is a reversible refrigeration machine. It can pump heat from the indoors outside for cooling just as any other airconditioner does, but by reversing the cycle during the winter, it can draw heat from the outside and deposit it indoors. Surprisingly, cold winter air does have heat in it, and the heat pump can extract that heat and make it usable.

Of course, as the outside temperature goes down, the efficiency of the heat pump declines as well. Compounding the problem is the fact that as outside temperature goes down, your heating load goes up. In conventional operation, when a heat pump can't handle the load by extracting enough heat from the outside air, supplemental electric resistance-heating coils built into the pump come to the rescue.

The efficiency of a heat pump is measured in its coefficient of performance (COP). COP is the amount of energy put out by the pump divided by the amount of energy put into it. If the heat pump is pulling 12,000 B.T.U.s of electrical energy and putting out 36,000 B.T.U.s of heat, the COP is three.

That means money saved. If your heat pump averages a COP of three, your electric bill will be one-third that if you used conventional electric resistance heating only. Unfortunately, as a practical matter, today's heat pumps run an annual COP average of 1.5 to 2.

But this is where solar energy can pay off. If the heat pump can be made to draw B.T.U.'s from a solar system during the cold days of winter instead of from the frigid outside air, then its COP goes up, and conventional energy consumption comes down. One method brings the

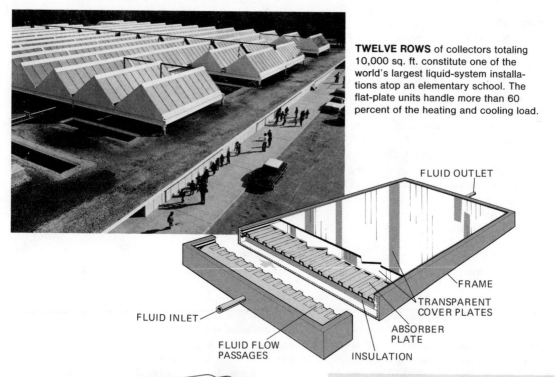

TWELVE ROWS of collectors totaling 10,000 sq. ft. constitute one of the world's largest liquid-system installations atop an elementary school. The flat-plate units handle more than 60 percent of the heating and cooling load.

FLUID OUTLET

FRAME

TRANSPARENT COVER PLATES

ABSORBER PLATE

INSULATION

FLUID INLET

FLUID FLOW PASSAGES

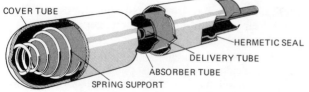

COVER TUBE

HERMETIC SEAL

DELIVERY TUBE

ABSORBER TUBE

SPRING SUPPORT

EVACUATED TUBULAR COLLECTOR

EACH UNIT in this townhouse group uses heat-pump-assisted solar energy for 60 percent of space heating and hot water. Evacuated tube collectors use liquid to transfer heat.

CONCENTRATORS and vacuum tubes above develop temperatures of 180° F. and up. Unit at right shows prismatic Fresnel lens that focuses sunlight on the copper absorber tube. A tracking device keeps the unit toward the sun.

COPPER ABSORBER TUBE

ANODIZED ALUMINUM REFLECTOR

HOUSING

FRESNEL LENS

INSULATION

CONCENTRATING COLLECTOR

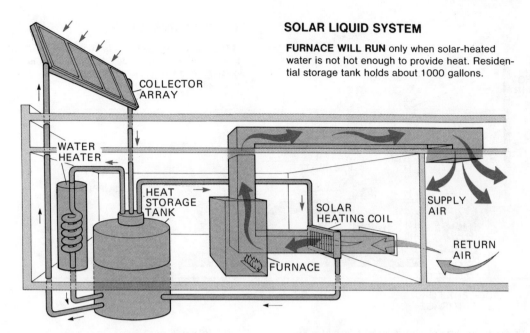

SOLAR LIQUID SYSTEM

FURNACE WILL RUN only when solar-heated water is not hot enough to provide heat. Residential storage tank holds about 1000 gallons.

COLLECTOR ARRAY

WATER HEATER

HEAT STORAGE TANK

SOLAR HEATING COIL

SUPPLY AIR

RETURN AIR

FURNACE

outside condenser coil inside. On cold days, solar-heated water is run through a heat exchanger near the coil unit causing it to operate as though it were removing heat from warm outside air. A duct system allows this coil to draw on outside air when the solar-heated water is not hot enough, as well as during the cooling season.

Other solar-assisted systems use water-to-water heat pumps. Whereas conventional heat pumps are air-to-air, this system allows the pump to draw directly from the solar storage tank.

Solar air-conditioning

While solar heating is coming of age, the use of solar energy for airconditioning is still in its infancy, but growing fast. Most units are in commercial buildings.

In solar airconditioning, an absorption chiller is used to convert hot to cold by evaporation. The more rapidly it takes place, the cooler you feel—the reason alcohol, for example, feels cool on the skin as it evaporates rapidly.

To operate effectively, absorption chillers need solar-heated water about 200° F. Such installations use high-temperature evacuated tube or concentrating collectors.

Evacuated tube collectors have a vacuum inside and a center pipe through which water flows. The vacuum causes the collector to act like a Thermos bottle and retain heat up to 600° F. Because of its shape, a tubular collector does not expose much of its surface to the sun and is, therefore, not as efficient when used in low-temperature operations.

Another way to go for high levels of heat from sunlight is to use concentrating collectors. These are shaped (generally in a U-type configuration) to concentrate sunlight onto a small area with lenses over the top of the collectors. They need direct sunlight to operate effectively, which means they must have tracking mechanisms to follow the sun across the sky. If you live where there is not much direct sunlight and therefore lower cooling loads, as in the Northeast, the use of concentrating collectors is hard to justify.

On the other hand, in the Southwest, where there is a lot of direct sunlight and a heavy cooling load, concentrating collectors reasonably can be used to drive absorption chillers.

Electricity from light

Two methods of converting sunlight to electricity are now being developed. One is the central power station concept where mirrors, concentrating sunlight on boilers, produce steam to drive electric generators. To date, this has been prohibitively expensive.

The second method uses on-site conversion devices called photovoltaic cells. They use one of two materials: silicon crystals, of which sand (a truly abundant fuel source) is a major component, or cadmium sulfide. While the latter is somewhat less expensive than silicon, it is also less efficient, and even with silicon cells a 10-percent efficiency is considered high.

Hot water kits

For the moment though, the largest application of solar energy is for domestic water heating. A number of kits on the market can be installed

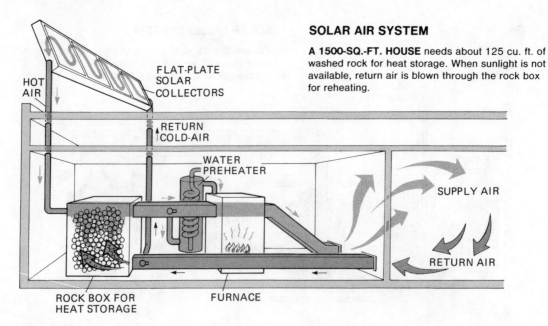

SOLAR AIR SYSTEM

A 1500-SQ.-FT. HOUSE needs about 125 cu. ft. of washed rock for heat storage. When sunlight is not available, return air is blown through the rock box for reheating.

with existing conventionally fired hot-water systems.

A space-heating system is more cost-effective in Chicago than in Miami. But even if solar heat is not competitive in your area now, it may be soon—as fuel costs go up and solar-equipment costs come down.

For this reason people now building homes are advised to design for solar retrofitting later, if they are not going to install it now. This involves designing for minimum use of energy, providing space for thermal storage equipment (water tank or rock box), and presenting a reasonable southern roof area for collectors.

Buyer beware

If you are planning to purchase a solar system in the near future—beware! There are systems out today that are making claims that are simply not true. Some even claim they are more than 100-percent efficient.

Check legislation

If you are planning to go solar, check local and national legislation. Many states have enacted legislation providing property, sales or income tax breaks for homeowners installing solar equipment.

CLIMATE AREAS FOR THE HEATING SEASON

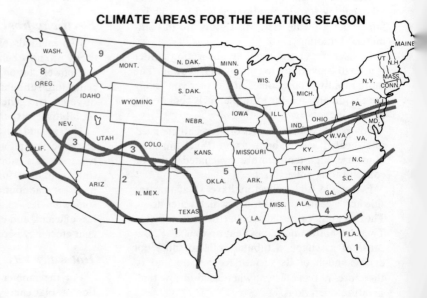

MEAN DAILY SOLAR RADIATION (LANGLEY)	HEATING DEGREE DAYS		
	0-2500	2500-5000	5000-9000
350-450	1	2	3
250-350	4	5	6
175-250	7	8	9

Chart shows relationship of heat load (degree days) and available solar energy (mean daily solar radiation). Areas that combine highest number of degree days with most langleys (units of solar radiation) will get most economical use from a solar system.

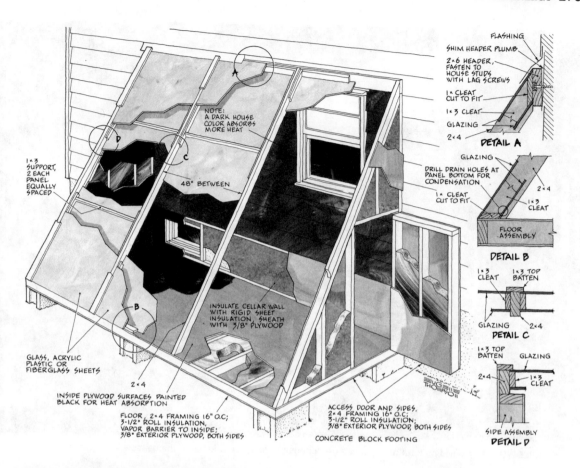

FLASHING
SHIM HEADER PLUMB
2×6 HEADER, FASTEN TO HOUSE STUDS WITH LAG SCREWS
1× CLEAT CUT TO FIT
1×3 CLEAT
GLAZING
2×4
DETAIL A

GLAZING
DRILL DRAIN HOLES AT PANEL BOTTOM FOR CONDENSATION
1× CLEAT CUT TO FIT
2×4
1×3 CLEAT
FLOOR ASSEMBLY
DETAIL B

1×3 CLEAT
1×3 TOP BATTEN
GLAZING
2×4
DETAIL C

1×3 TOP BATTEN
GLAZING
2×4
1×3 CLEAT
SIDE ASSEMBLY
DETAIL D

NOTE: A DARK HOUSE COLOR ABSORBS MORE HEAT

1×3 SUPPORT, 2 EACH PANEL EQUALLY SPACED

48" BETWEEN

INSULATE CELLAR WALL WITH RIGID SHEET INSULATION, SHEATH WITH 3/8" PLYWOOD

GLASS, ACRYLIC PLASTIC OR FIBERGLASS SHEETS

2×4

INSIDE PLYWOOD SURFACES PAINTED BLACK FOR HEAT ABSORPTION

FLOOR, 2×4 FRAMING 16" O.C.; 3-1/2" ROLL INSULATION, VAPOR BARRIER TO INSIDE; 3/8" EXTERIOR PLYWOOD, BOTH SIDES

ACCESS DOOR AND SIDES, 2×4 FRAMING 16" O.C.; 3-1/2" ROLL INSULATION; 3/8" EXTERIOR PLYWOOD, BOTH SIDES

CONCRETE BLOCK FOOTING

Solar collector anyone can build

■ THIS PASSIVE COLLECTOR is simply a double-glazed lean-to adjoining the south-facing wall of a house. As air is heated, it passes through an open window or vent at the top of the enclosure. Cooler air, drawn in through a basement window or vent, replaces the hot air. No active systems are involved—just convection (the transfer of heat by the movement of air). To prevent heat buildup in the summer, the collector is covered with white-painted plywood panels.

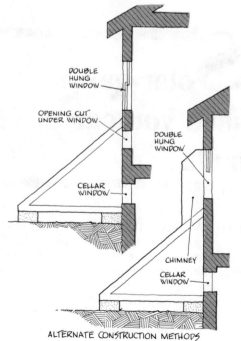

DOUBLE HUNG WINDOW
OPENING CUT UNDER WINDOW
CELLAR WINDOW
DOUBLE HUNG WINDOW
CHIMNEY
CELLAR WINDOW

ALTERNATE CONSTRUCTION METHODS

QUAINT BUILDING features sliding barn doors plus a greenhouse to give you a jump on the season.

Solar garden shed you can build

■ THE ATTRACTIVE SHED shown in detail on these pages is built using conventional building techniques and a minimum of material. What's different about this backyard shed is that it serves two purposes:

● Its generous size lets it hold all the gardening tools you are likely to own, plus a small tractor.

● The easy-build greenhouse lets you get started early in the season—so you are sure of an early harvest for many of the crops.

Construct the walls one at a time, tipping each up into position as it's assembled. You'll need a helper to lift the wall and hold it steady while you check both vertical planes with a spirit level. When wall is plumb, use two diagonal braces to hold it until other walls are placed.

It's built on skids

The shed is built on skids rather than on a permanent foundation. First, the building can be moved with tractor and cable if desired, so that ground usage can be rotated. Second, in many areas of the country a backyard building, erected over permanent footing and block walls requires a permit. A shed on skids usually doesn't. Check your building department.

Because the building rests on the ground, use pressure-treated lumber for the skids and all flooring.

Conventional framing is used throughout. The easiest way to assemble such a shed of this type is to build the floor first and use it as a work platform for the walls.

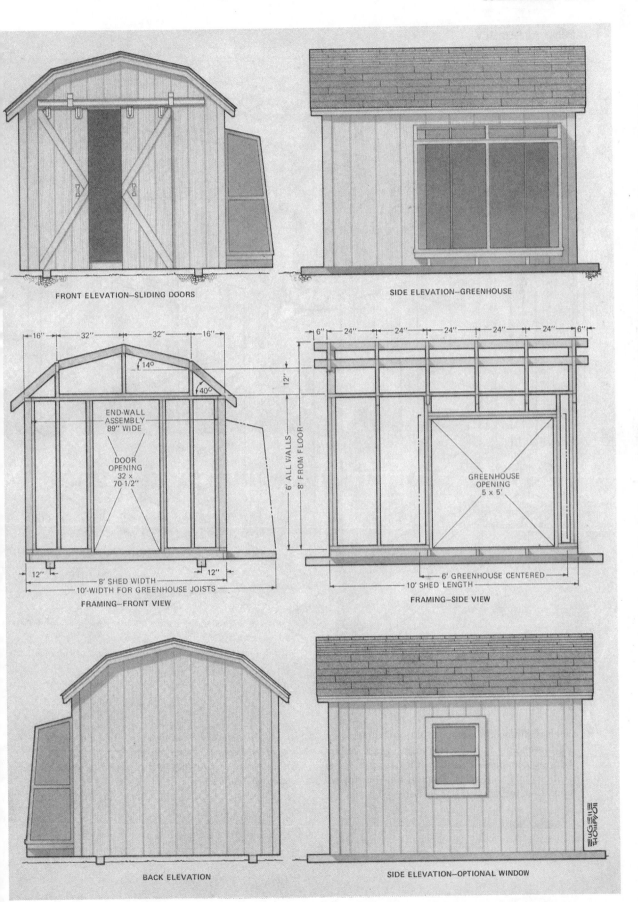

FRONT ELEVATION—SLIDING DOORS

SIDE ELEVATION—GREENHOUSE

16" — 32" — 32" — 16"

14°

40°

END-WALL
ASSEMBLY
89" WIDE

DOOR
OPENING
32 x
70-1/2"

12"

6' ALL WALLS

8' FROM FLOOR

12" — 12"

8' SHED WIDTH
10' WIDTH FOR GREENHOUSE JOISTS

FRAMING—FRONT VIEW

6" — 24" — 24" — 24" — 24" — 6"

GREENHOUSE
OPENING
5 x 5'

6' GREENHOUSE CENTERED
10' SHED LENGTH

FRAMING—SIDE VIEW

BACK ELEVATION

SIDE ELEVATION—OPTIONAL WINDOW

FRAMING ASSEMBLY

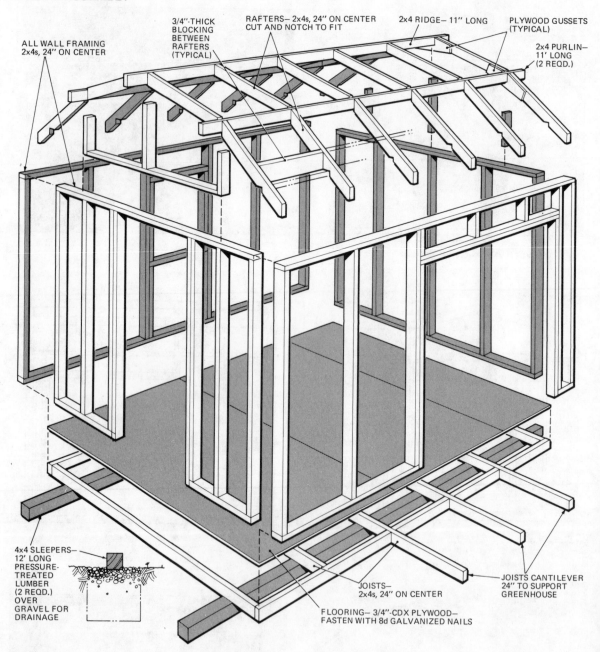

ALL WALL FRAMING 2x4s, 24" ON CENTER

3/4"-THICK BLOCKING BETWEEN RAFTERS (TYPICAL)

RAFTERS— 2x4s, 24" ON CENTER CUT AND NOTCH TO FIT

2x4 RIDGE— 11" LONG

PLYWOOD GUSSETS (TYPICAL)

2x4 PURLIN— 11' LONG (2 REQD.)

4x4 SLEEPERS— 12' LONG PRESSURE-TREATED LUMBER (2 REQD.) OVER GRAVEL FOR DRAINAGE

JOISTS— 2x4s, 24" ON CENTER

FLOORING— 3/4"-CDX PLYWOOD— FASTEN WITH 8d GALVANIZED NAILS

JOISTS CANTILEVER 24" TO SUPPORT GREENHOUSE

Next, frame the gambrel roof. A ridgeboard, purlins and plywood gussets ensure good weight-bearing capabilities. Install the two end rafter sections first to hold ridgeboard and purlins secure, then the other rafter sections.

Skin the walls with exterior plywood and the roof with ⅜-in., sheathing-grade plywood. Once the walls are covered with plywood, remove the diagonal braces.

Door hardware is available at hardware stores.

SIDING, ROOFING AND GREENHOUSE DETAILS

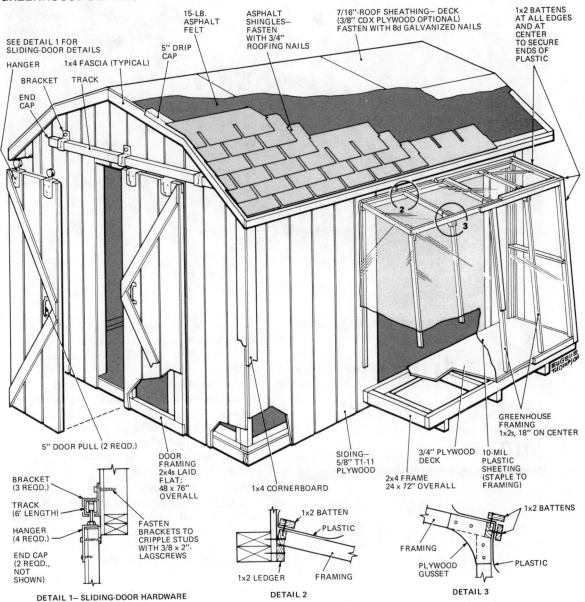

15-LB. ASPHALT FELT

ASPHALT SHINGLES— FASTEN WITH 3/4" ROOFING NAILS

7/16"-ROOF SHEATHING— DECK (3/8" CDX PLYWOOD OPTIONAL) FASTEN WITH 8d GALVANIZED NAILS

1x2 BATTENS AT ALL EDGES AND AT CENTER TO SECURE ENDS OF PLASTIC

SEE DETAIL 1 FOR SLIDING-DOOR DETAILS

5" DRIP CAP

HANGER

1x4 FASCIA (TYPICAL)

BRACKET   TRACK

END CAP

5" DOOR PULL (2 REQD.)

DOOR FRAMING 2x4s LAID FLAT; 48 x 76" OVERALL

1x4 CORNERBOARD

SIDING— 5/8" T1-11 PLYWOOD

3/4" PLYWOOD DECK

2x4 FRAME 24 x 72" OVERALL

10-MIL PLASTIC SHEETING (STAPLE TO FRAMING)

GREENHOUSE FRAMING 1x2s, 18" ON CENTER

BRACKET (3 REQD.)

TRACK (6' LENGTH)

HANGER (4 REQD.)

END CAP (2 REQD., NOT SHOWN)

FASTEN BRACKETS TO CRIPPLE STUDS WITH 3/8 x 2"- LAGSCREWS

DETAIL 1— SLIDING-DOOR HARDWARE

1x2 BATTEN

PLASTIC

1x2 LEDGER   FRAMING

DETAIL 2

1x2 BATTENS

FRAMING

PLYWOOD GUSSET

PLASTIC

DETAIL 3

Cover the roof with overlapped layers of 15-lb. felt followed by 235-lb. asphalt shingles with self-sealing edges. Apply a coat of exterior stain to the outside of the plywood.

The greenhouse cover is of 10-mil polyethyl-ene sheet plastic, available at lumberyards and home centers.

If you'd like to move the shed in your yard, in-stall a hefty eyebolt through the end joist so you can pull it easily with cable and tractor.

Pure drinking water from the sun

■ THIS SOLAR STILL, operating on the simple principles of evaporation and condensation, will remove *all* impurities from about one gallon of water a day.

Build the still box first. It should face south and receive full sun. If it's necessary to mount the unit on the sloped surface of the roof, cut the back end (CC) 21 in. high and the front (BB) 6 in. high, plus whatever is required so that the pan supports will be level.

Bore holes for the supply and return lines in the plywood bottom (AA). Also bore two 1-in.-dia. weep holes, one at each end. Screen these to keep out insects.

Frame comes next

Next, build the frame for the still's lid and a platform for the supply tank. Prime all wood components with top-quality wood primer, then apply two coats of high-quality exterior latex enamel.

Give the evaporation pans two coats of rust-resistant paint that is nontoxic and adheres to galvanized surfaces. Plumb the system as shown in the drawings. A handsaw can be used to cut the trough in half (after assembly).

With help, take the unit up on the roof and position it where it will receive full sun, then make final connections.

If it's installed on a roof slope, attach a 2x4 cleat to the roof at the lower end of the still. Use lagscrews in the rafters and apply ample sealant at the holes. Run braided guy wires from the sides of the still to the eave. These will anchor the still. Install turnbuckles, but do not tighten the turnbuckles yet.

Run the supply-line tubing to a convenient water supply and connect through a valve. The output line should not be connected to the storage tank at this time.

Spread aquarium gravel

Lay a small piece of screen over the openings in the evaporation pans, then spread a layer of black aquarium gravel over the surface of the pans. Since the evaporation of the water will deposit light-colored minerals in the pans, stir the black gravel periodically.

To prevent the growth of microorganisms in

the tank and pans, put a quarter pound of copper sulfate crystals in the supply tank.

When you're ready to activate the system, turn on the water supply. As the water begins to run into the evaporation pans, use shims to attain the final level of the unit. Adjust the water level in the pans by bending the shaft of the float valve (Bobby valve). The float should stop the flow when the water just covers the gravel. At this point, tighten the turnbuckles on the braided anchor wires.

Weatherstrip the cleats

Next, apply weatherstripping to the bottom of the glass-support cleats (PP and QQ). Put the lid with glass in place on the box and attach with wood screws. Water will condense on the glass and drip off the silicone bead into the trough.

Let the still run for three days before collecting the distilled water for use. During this time, find a convenient location for the insulated picnic cooler that serves as a storage tank and install an overflow tube in it. Seal the points where the tubing passes through the walls of the cooler with clear silicone.

Set the timer

Run plastic tubing from the air pump, through the lid of the cooler, to the air stone and seal with silicone once again. Set the timer so that the air pump runs for about three hours in the evening.

Once the still has run for three days, pass the output line through the lid of the cooler; use silicone to seal the joint. Before use, let the cooler fill a day or two to provide a buffer supply of water.

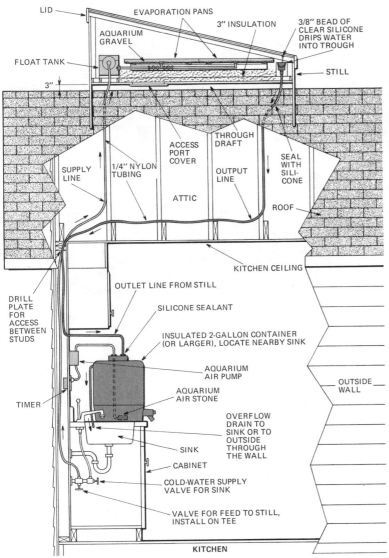

MAKE BOX for still of exterior-grade plywood. Use resorcinol glue at joints. Cut V-notch to suit roof pitch.

USE ½-in. PVC pipe to make feeder lines from the supply tank to the black evaporation pans. Use brass drains.

SUPPLY TANK, with float valve (Bobby valve), controls water level in the still and is connected to cold-water supply.

MATERIALS LIST—SOLAR STILL

Key	No.	Size and description (use)
A	1	Robert Bobby valve (float valve) with ¼" tubing fitting
B	1	2"-dia. float (for Bobby valve)
C	5	Brass evaporative cooler drains
D	5	Brass evaporative cooler-drain locks
E	5	Evaporative cooler-drain rubber washers
F	9	½ × ½" PVC male pipe-thread adapters
G	1	½" × length to suit PVC pipe (feeder line)
H	1	½" PVC cross fitting
I	9	½" PVC nipples
J	2	½" galvanized unions
K	1	½" PVC tee
L	4	½" PVC elbows
M	2	2" PVC caps (collecting-trough ends)
N	1	2" PVC tee (collecting-trough drain)
O	1	2 × 36" PVC pipe (collecting trough)
P	1	½ × 2" PVC female pipe-thread reducer
Q	1	Compression fitting
R	*	¼" nylon or soft copper tubing (supply and output tubing)
S	*	Glazier's points
T	*	No. 6 × 1" Phillips-head screws
U	*	3d galvanized box nails
V	4	¼"-dia. screw eyes or eyebolts with washers and nuts
W	2	Turnbuckles
X	1	5 × 6 × 12" plastic ice-cube storage tray (float tank)
Y	4	1 × 17½ × 23½" galvanized automotive drip pan (evaporation pans)
Z	1	20 lbs. aquarium gravel
AA	1	½ × 37 × 63" exterior plywood (bottom)
BB	1	½ × 37" × height to suit (overall) exterior plywood (front support)
CC	1	½ × 37" × height to suit (overall) exterior plywood (back support)
DD	2	½ × 21 × 64" (overall) exterior plywood (sides)
EE	1	½ × 12 × 13" exterior plywood (access port cover)
FF	2	¾ × 3½ × 66" pine (sides of top)
GG	2	¾ × 3½ × 38½" pine (front, back of top)
HH	2	¾ × 1½ × 63" pine (cleats)
II	2	¾ × 1½ × 19" (overall) pine (back cleats)
JJ	2	¾ × 1½ × 35½" pine (front and back bottom cleats)
KK	2	¾ × 1½ × 4" pine (front supports)
LL	2	¾ × 1½ × 2⅝" pine (filler block)
MM	2	¾ × 3½ × 4" pine (collecting-trough supports)
NN	2	¾ × 1½ × 44" pine (evaporation-pan supports)
OO	4	¾ × 1½ × 37" pine (evaporation-pan supports)
PP	2	¾ × 1½ × 63" pine (glass supports)
QQ	2	¾ × 1½ × 38½" pine (glass supports)
RR	1	⅛ × 38⅜ × 64⅜" double-strength glass
SS	8	2" corner braces
TT	1	½" × ¾" × 18' adhesive-backed foam weather-stripping
UU	2	¾ × 1½ × 12" pine (float-tank supports)
VV	2	¾ × 1½ × 3¾" pine (float-tank supports)
WW	1	¾ × 5¼ × 12" pine (float-tank platform)

Misc.: ⅛" braided galvanized guy wire as reqd., 3" fiberglass batt insulation, silicone sealant, insulated 2-gal. container, timer, aquarium air pump, aquarium air stone, in-line valve.
*As required.

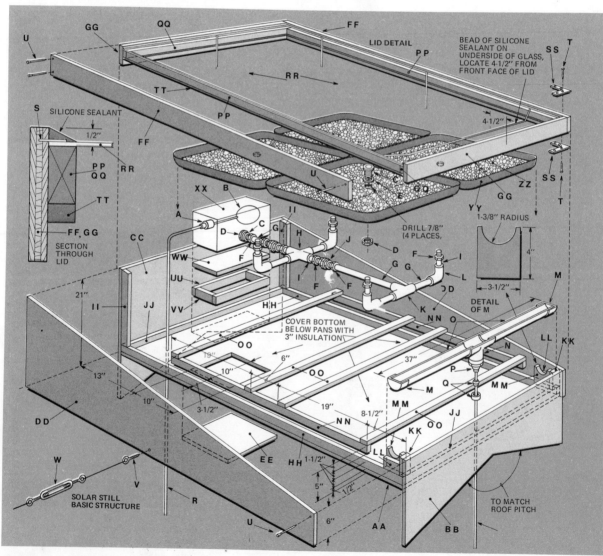

Kiln-dry your lumber with solar heat

■ TO BEAT THE COST of small quantities of kiln-dried hardwoods, you can dry your own green wood using solar energy. This model has an 800-board-foot capacity. Collectors on this version have been rotated on their 40°-from-vertical axes to collect more early-morning and later-afternoon sun.

Collectors on this version have been rotated on their 40°-from-vertical axes to collect more early-morning and later-afternoon sun.

Operating in southern Wisconsin (43° north latitude), the kiln can dry a load of 1-in.-thick (4/4) walnut from 85-percent moisture to 8 percent (same as kiln-dried and right for interior use) in 50 summer days, with the interior temperature often reaching 130° F. Wintertime dry-ing does take considerably longer, but output can be upped by starting with air-dried wood.

Operation of this solar kiln is simple. Solar collectors fitted 1½ in. behind glazed sash are broad, flat ducts—black-painted sheet metal on the side facing the glass and ⅛-in. hardboard on the other. Air enters the collectors through floor vents cut off from the interior by plastic film. Warmed air rises in the collectors, escapes out the tops, and is circulated through the stacked and spaced wood by two thermostatically governed fans (set to go on at 80° F.) Electricity for the fans is the only operating expense.

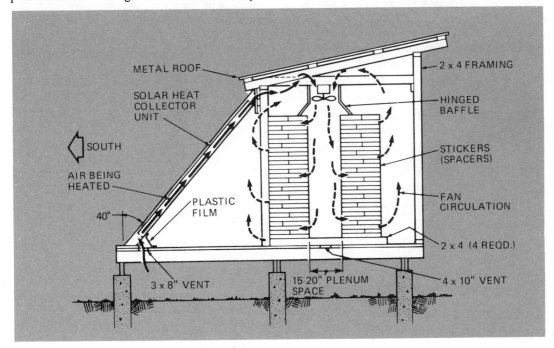

Hot water from the sun

■ WHEN YOU'VE DONE all you can to cut energy use and waste in your home, the only way to trim those bills more is to *add* energy somehow. One way to do that—without spending your life's savings—is to install a solar domestic hot-water system.

Solar hot water is relatively easy to retrofit. A small collector array can go on the roof, against a wall, or on a separate support frame in the yard—while solar space heating requires a collector area equal to one-third to one-half the floor area to be heated. You need a large, strong, properly angled roof for such an array.

A study, done a number of years ago, when fuels were cheaper, has shown that solar water heating, at a total system cost of $20 per square foot of collector, is cost-effective in most parts of the country, beating electric resistance heating in all but one of the 13 cities considered. Payback time (system cost divided by annual savings) ranged from 9 to 13 years in the other 12. The payback period will keep getting shorter as conventional-energy prices go up.

If new technology and government incentives combine to reduce system costs, solar hot water and solar space heating will then be competitive with all conventional fuels.

System basics

The collector is the guts of any solar system. As commonly used for solar hot water, it has an absorber plate covered with a special selective surface or painted flat black to collect light and convert it to heat, plus tubing attached to the plate to carry the heat-transfer medium (water, water plus antifreeze, or air) that gathers the absorbed heat and takes it to the point of use. The absorber plate is enclosed in an insulated frame and covered with glass or transparent plastic.

Collectors should be pitched at an angle equal to local latitude, but a variation of 10° either way (to suit a roof's pitch, for example) can be accepted—and in some cases it can pay to tip them forward to pick up sunlight by reflection from a horizontal surface. This can be especially effective in areas of the country that have snow cover for most of the winter. Similarly, collectors are usually oriented to point due south, but variation of up to 20° either way is acceptable and may be necessary to make the installation practical.

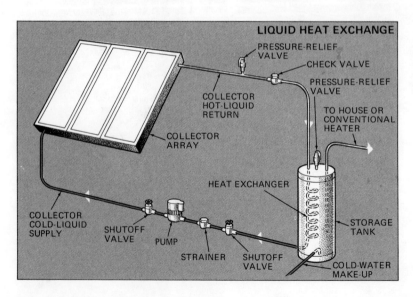

LIQUID HEAT EXCHANGE

PRESSURE-RELIEF VALVE
CHECK VALVE
PRESSURE-RELIEF VALVE
COLLECTOR HOT-LIQUID RETURN
TO HOUSE OR CONVENTIONAL HEATER
COLLECTOR ARRAY
HEAT EXCHANGER
COLLECTOR COLD-LIQUID SUPPLY
SHUTOFF VALVE
PUMP
STRAINER
SHUTOFF VALVE
STORAGE TANK
COLD-WATER MAKE-UP

LIQUID MEDIUM in collectors won't freeze since it's an antifreeze solution—but there must be absolutely no mixing of antifreeze with domestic water supply.

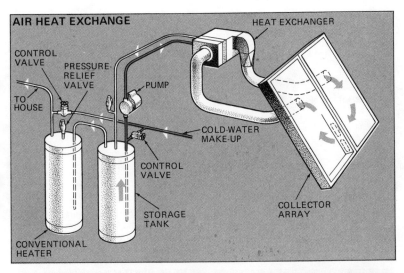

AIR HEAT EXCHANGE

HEAT EXCHANGER

CONTROL VALVE

PRESSURE-RELIEF VALVE

PUMP

TO HOUSE

COLD-WATER MAKE-UP

CONTROL VALVE

STORAGE TANK

COLLECTOR ARRAY

CONVENTIONAL HEATER

USING AIR as a heat-exchange medium eliminates both the hazard of collector freeze-up and the danger of contamination of house water with antifreeze.

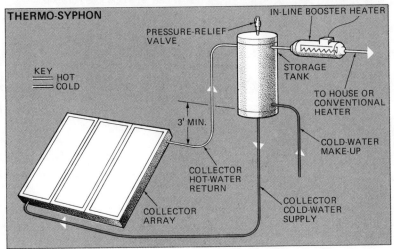

THERMO-SYPHON

IN-LINE BOOSTER HEATER

PRESSURE-RELIEF VALVE

KEY
HOT
COLD

STORAGE TANK

TO HOUSE OR CONVENTIONAL HEATER

3' MIN.

COLD-WATER MAKE-UP

COLLECTOR HOT-WATER RETURN

COLLECTOR COLD-WATER SUPPLY

COLLECTOR ARRAY

ESSENTIALLY PASSIVE system relies on gravity and convection to circulate water: Cold water flows from bottom of tank to bottom of collector, returns when warmed.

Other factors that need attention are shading of collectors by trees or parts of the house and snow accumulation on the array.

A solar hot-water system is really a preheater, using conventional heating to give the water a final boost to the desired temperature. It requires much less conventional energy than a normal system. Most solar systems use a separate storage tank that supplies the tank of a conventional heater—which also provides backup for night and for cloudy days.

Five systems

With all the many kits and components coming onto the market, there are still just five basic types of solar hot-water systems in common use.

Simplest is the thermo-siphon setup, which de-pends on gravity and convection to circulate water through its collectors. It requires a water storage tank located near and slightly above the collector array. Such a system is fine where there's plenty of sunshine and the temperature rarely dips to 32° F., but in most parts of the country, water can freeze and wreck the whole works. Frequent manual draining—a nuisance—or a resistance booster heater can prevent freeze-ups, but flow rate and temperatures remain difficult to control in a thermo-siphon system.

The four other systems allow a more remote tank location. In the draindown type, a pump moves water through the collectors only when there's enough sunlight to prevent freezing and to produce useful heat. At other times, the pump is automatically shut off and the collectors are simultaneously drained.

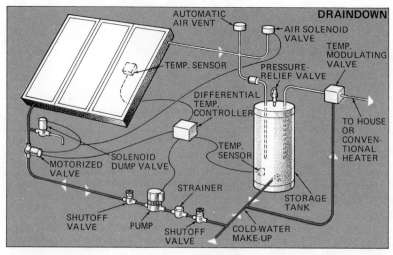

DRAINDOWN

AUTOMATIC AIR VENT

AIR SOLENOID VALVE

TEMP. MODULATING VALVE

TEMP. SENSOR

PRESSURE-RELIEF VALVE

DIFFERENTIAL TEMP. CONTROLLER

TO HOUSE OR CONVENTIONAL HEATER

TEMP. SENSOR

MOTORIZED VALVE

SOLENOID DUMP VALVE

STRAINER

STORAGE TANK

SHUTOFF VALVE

PUMP

SHUTOFF VALVE

COLD-WATER MAKE-UP

ELABORATE CONTROLS are needed to assure automatic drainage of collectors and pump cutoff when temperature falls to freezing or collectors can't warm water.

SIMPLER SYSTEM loses efficiency because water must be heated to keep it moving through collectors during periods of below-freezing temperatures.

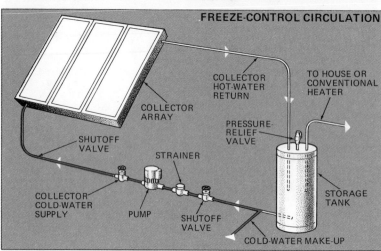

FREEZE-CONTROL CIRCULATION

COLLECTOR HOT-WATER RETURN

TO HOUSE OR CONVENTIONAL HEATER

COLLECTOR ARRAY

PRESSURE-RELIEF VALVE

SHUTOFF VALVE

STRAINER

COLLECTOR COLD-WATER SUPPLY

PUMP

SHUTOFF VALVE

STORAGE TANK

COLD-WATER MAKE-UP

A less common system uses what's called freeze-control circulation from storage. Warm water is kept moving in the collectors when the temperature drops to freezing. It's less efficient than a draindown system because it uses heat to warm the collectors, but it gives the advantage of simpler controls.

Using antifreeze

An obvious way to keep collectors from freezing is not to run plain water through them. You can use an antifreeze solution instead and make this liquid surrender its gathered heat to the water through a heat exchanger, usually a coil of tubing inside or around the outside of the tank. But this requires care. Most antifreezes are poison, and some local codes require a double-wall heat exchanger to keep house water and collector medium separate. The antifreeze solution also must be replaced periodically as it tends to become corrosive.

The heat-exchanger idea can also be used with air as the medium. Water from the tank is pumped out to a motorized heat exchanger, then returns to the tank. Both liquid and air heat-exchange setups are less efficient than heating the water directly, but they do eliminate the freezing problem.

Cautions: Regardless of the system you're considering, be wary when shopping for solar equipment—some manufacturers make impossible claims. Ask anyone who wants to sell you solar equipment for names of other customers, and check with them. Get a guarantee, too. Systems can vary greatly in cost, yet work about equally well. How long they'll last is the question that's still hard to answer. Tests being performed now in many areas of the country may soon yield the answer.

Solar water heater you can build

THIS SOLAR water heater can supply at least 46 gallons of hot water on sunny days.

■ THE SOLAR WATER PANEL must face directly south. Its angle (degree of pitch) depends on its geographic location and latitude. Note: In freezing climates, the solar heater must have a cold-water bypass that runs to the existing heater, because the solar-heating system must drain.

Aluminum solar fins on the copper tubes conduct absorbed solar heat to water in the tubes. Water circulating by thermo-siphon action keeps warm water rising to a 42-gal. insulated storage tank above the panel. This water feeds to the existing water heater.

Begin by boring holes for the tubes in the headers and reaming them to exact size. Clean the ends of the tube with steel wool in order to assure good solder contact; solder all tubes to one header first. Solder the brass plugs in place.

The simple cover has a groove for wedges glued to secure the vinyl sheet. Fishing line passed over the vinyl, then passed through holes

bored in the cover frame, with the ends wound around nails, helps hold the vinyl.

To insert the headers in the frame, elongate the frame holes and slide the headers in at an angle. Later, you can fill the holes.

A simple die of a 2-in. oak cube helps shape the solar fins. Bore a $^{13}/_{32}$-in.-dia. hole in the wood and cut through the hole lengthwise so that $^5/_{16}$ in. of the diameter remains. Shape the fin to the block's contour with a $^3/_8$-in.-dia. steel rod. Press-fit the fins on the underside of the tubes and spray-paint the metal black. Fasten the cover and install the panel securely.

MATERIALS LIST—SOLAR HEATER

Key	No.	Size and description (use)
A	2*	1⅛" o.d. x 53" type "L" copper tubing (headers)
B	15*	⅜" o.d. x 57⅞" type "L" copper tubing
C	2*	¾ x 3½ x 49" redwood (frame)
D	2	¾ x 3½ x 63" redwood (frame)
E	2*	¾ x 1¼ x 50½" redwood (cover)
F	2	¾ x 1¼ x 64½" redwood (cover)
G	1*	⅛ x 48 x 62" hardboard (frame bottom)
H	1*	¾" x 6 sq. ft. Styrofoam insulation sheeting
I	1	8-mil vinyl sheet
J	1	⅛ x ⅜" x 20'* redwood (wedges)
K	120*	2 x 4³/₃₂" x 22-ga. aluminum sheet, 10 sq. ft. (fins)
L	2	¹/₁₆ x 1.025"-dia. brass discs (end plugs)
M	1	42-gal. storage tank with insulation
N	4	3 x 4 x 4" sheet-metal angles (corner reinforcements)
O	4	1 x 4 x 4" sheet-metal angles (corner reinforcements)
P	48	¾" No. 10 sheet-metal screws
Q	†	Braided steel fishing line (secure vinyl)
R	†	Nail to secure fishing line ends

Misc.: 1½" No. 8 fh woodscrews, flat, black heat-resistant paint, solder, professional cabinetmaker's contact cement.
* Increase by the number of increments that the unit will be enlarged. † As required.

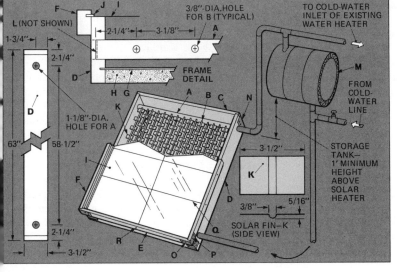

AUTHOR CHECKS lines on the completed installation. The compass (inset) shows panel relation to true south.

Solar water heater installation

■ IN A CLOSED-LOOP solar fluid system, a transfer fluid transports heat from sun rays to the water heater where a heat exchanger transfers it from solar fluid to the potable water. An alternative is to run the potable water through the lines and collector plates, and back to the water heater.

Department of Energy figures rate solar efficiency less than 50 percent efficient in the area near New York City. There, you need a backup system for sunless days and periods of heavy water use.

Choosing collectors

Solar collector panels may be almost out of sight on the roof, but you should give them spe-cial thought. These plates can be exposed to severe temperature extremes. A flat-plate collector can be hit with temperatures below 0° F. on winter nights and over 400° F. (if not operating) on summer days. And they contend with wind, snow, sleet, rain and hail. Although there is similarity in operating principles of many solar domestic hot-water systems, each maker has certain unique or unusual features.

Laying out your panels

Collectors should be placed to receive un-shaded sun during the "solar day"—9:00 a.m. to 3:00 p.m. Check your roof to see that trees or neighbors' homes won't shade your collectors. Remember, the sun changes position significantly. In winter, for example, it is much closer to the horizon and casts longer shadows.

Don't position collectors near the roof ridge because of a greater risk of damage by high winds. Locate the plates with horizontal mid-lines slightly below mid-height of the sloped roof. Keep plates close as possible to storage tanks to reduce heat loss during circulation of solar fluid.

Make certain you or your contractor check that hazards aren't created for house occupants. Points to think about:

● Antifreeze fluid, waterproofing and insulation

should comply with local codes for fire safety and health under operating and nonoperating conditions.

● Storage tanks and piping that may reach temperatures above 140° F. should be insulated so passersby will not be burned should they contact those elements. Identify pressure and temperature relief valves with appropriate warnings.

● The system should withstand pressures of 150 pounds per square inch. The hot-water side should be protected against excessive temperatures.

INSTALLING THE COLLECTOR-PLATE HARDWARE

SOLID FASTENING for collector hardware is a must. Here, cat is located.

USE 16D NAILS to secure the cat. See drawings for blocking technique.

ALL BRACKETS on the job were lag-screwed into rafters, cats or blocking.

HOW THE SYSTEM WORKS

Hot rays from the sun are absorbed by the roof-mounted collector panels to heat a special antifreeze fluid that circulates through integral copper channels. The propylene glycol eliminates any chance of freezing in cold climates during the unit's downtime (i.e., at night). The system utilizes a closed-loop design for transfer of heated solution of the preheater and its return. The heater-mounted differential controller has a modulating output (speeds up or slows down glycol solar fluid flow depending on available energy) to collect the maximum amount of heat from the solar panels, even on cloudy days.

The house water service flows to the preheater tank in which the heat exchanger is submerged. The heat exchanger is double-walled and electrically isolated from the tank for safety. As the solar fluid flows through the exchanger, the heat is transferred through double-walled pipes of the exchanger to the domestic water supply.

Installation can include an electric backup heat system as shown. This unit fires up to bring water temperature to preset use temperature, usually from 120° to 140° F. You can eliminate the electric backup system and install a backup gas heater and water tank instead.

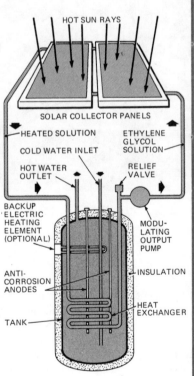

SECOND bottom bracket is located so that blocking can be installed inside.

NEXT, the collector is hoisted to the roof and secured to brackets.

SINCE ROOF is pitched 42°, short legs at top bring panels to desirable 45°.

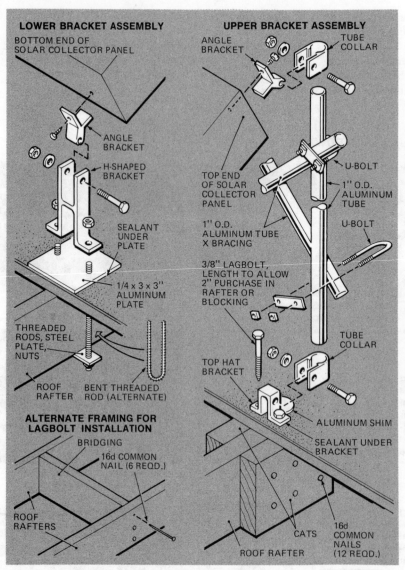

LOWER BRACKET ASSEMBLY

BOTTOM END OF SOLAR COLLECTOR PANEL

ANGLE BRACKET

H-SHAPED BRACKET

SEALANT UNDER PLATE

1/4 x 3 x 3" ALUMINUM PLATE

THREADED RODS, STEEL PLATE, NUTS

ROOF RAFTER

BENT THREADED ROD (ALTERNATE)

ALTERNATE FRAMING FOR LAGBOLT INSTALLATION

BRIDGING

16d COMMON NAIL (6 REQD.)

ROOF RAFTERS

UPPER BRACKET ASSEMBLY

ANGLE BRACKET

TUBE COLLAR

U-BOLT

TOP END OF SOLAR COLLECTOR PANEL

1" O.D. ALUMINUM TUBE

1" O.D. ALUMINUM TUBE X BRACING

U-BOLT

3/8" LAGBOLT, LENGTH TO ALLOW 2" PURCHASE IN RAFTER OR BLOCKING

TUBE COLLAR

TOP HAT BRACKET

ALUMINUM SHIM

SEALANT UNDER BRACKET

CATS

ROOF RAFTER

16d COMMON NAILS (12 REQD.)

DRAWINGS (left) show the standard panel installation method that was used. When bracket misses a rafter, you must install either cats or blocking.

AUTHOR FOUND collector weight tilted brackets, which then cut into shingles.

A ¼ x 3 x 5-IN. aluminum plate under the bracket distributed the weight.

● Equipment design should fully protect the potable water supply.

Installing the system

Ripping out the old heater and installing plates, preheater and tank with gas heater took three people 3½ days. Contractors experienced with a system's installation could cut the labor time to two days for three people and reduce installation costs.

Any quality manufacturer will help you determine the most efficient collector panel direction and tilt for your area. The optimum orientation of a collector in the Northern Hemisphere is true south or slightly west of it, but variations 20° east or west of true south are acceptable. The angle of inclination (tilt) needed equals the latitude of the location (in degrees) measured from the horizontal, plus or minus 10°. Since optimum tilt for this site is 45°, the plates could have been installed flat on the 42°-sloped roof. But short legs were added at the top to get a 45° tilt angle.

INSTALLING THE SOLAR FLUID LINE

COPPER PIPING for solar fluid was run on the outside of house.

PIPE ELBOWS around gutters. Straight run requires holes through cornice.

TO MINIMIZE heat loss as fluid travels, pipe must be wrapped with insulation.

ARMAFLEX taped around elbows prevents heat loss at these points, too.

ALL JOINTS are soldered to eliminate joint hardware and the chance of leaks.

PLUMBER did some soldering on roof to end the need to lift assembled sections.

IMPRESSIVE ARRAY of gauges (more than maker calls for, in fact) provide these readings: **A,** Pressure/temperature of preheated water to water heater; in closed loop—**B,** pressure/temperature of fluid collectors; **C,** pressure/temperature, fluid to preheater; **D,** line pressure. **E** senses temperature differential between sensor in preheater and sensor mounted on collector plates and turns on circulator **F** to vary the flow of the solar fluid depending upon the available energy.

Solar system heat pump-water heater

■ APPROXIMATELY 15 PERCENT of a home electric bill can go to heat water. Yours could be higher. While this cost may not break the bank, it is a continuing year-round expense. Many people looking to save on energy costs find themselves in a morass of new and innovative water-heating products. Some of these work, some don't; others have such a long payback period that it hardly matters whether they work or not.

A solar-assisted, heat-pump water-heating system was tested. Savings added up to about 300 to 400 kilowatt hours per month.

The first component installed was one of the new hot-water heat pumps. These air-to-water devices are touted to cut the cost of heating water dramatically, whether you live in Alaska or Alabama. They operate by removing some of the heat from the surrounding air and using it to heat water.

Next, two separate systems were added that heat water with solar energy. The first consists of three collector panels mounted on the roof. The second makes use of two porcelain-lined tempering tanks suspended from the trusses in an attic. Potable water circulates through both systems, and each operates independently of the other. Because of the experimental nature of this project, both were installed; most people would use one or the other.

Keep in mind that going solar in the northern latitudes is not always economically beneficial. Since the house used in the test is in northern Illinois, the plan was to use the solar parts of the system primarily during the summer months. You'll save more with a year-round system, but there are several benefits to a warm-weather-only system: To begin with, summer is the time of year when many utilities raise their rates because of the huge increases in demand. In northern Illinois, this rate increase is about 19 percent. Second, summer is also the time when most families use more hot water: They shower and launder more frequently during hot, sticky weather.

The last advantage is strictly an investment consideration. A summer-only system eliminates the need for a closed-loop arrangement, which requires antifreeze to keep the circulating fluid from freezing, and a heat exchanger, to remove heat from the toxic antifreeze line and apply it to a second line containing potable water. The antifreeze, additional plumbing and heat exchanger add substantially to the startup costs and simultaneously reduce the overall efficiency of the system by some 15 to 20 percent.

How the system works

The drawing gives the best layout for the entire system. The best way to understand it is to follow the water, step by step, as it moves through the various components.

To begin with, there is a 267-ft.-deep well to supply water with very high mineral content to a pressure tank (A).

This hardness is not only a problem for everyday home use, but also represents a distinct liability for the new installation. The minute iron and other mineral particles suspended in the water could raise havoc with the small, narrow tubes in the collector panels, the heat pump, circulating pump and the many valves in the system. To prevent this, the minerals are removed by a water softener [E]. This device exchanges salt for the minerals in the water, protecting the components farther down the line.

But there are a couple of drawbacks to using the softening system. First, many physicians today discourage the use of excess salt because it is believed to contribute to high blood pressure, and second, salt treatment of the water is an added expense.

To offset both of these concerns, hot water was diverted to two places before it went to the softener. The first was the outside spigots that provide water for gardening and lawn care. The second diverted water to a separate faucet at the kitchen sink. Water passes through a charcoal filter [C] that removes particles as small as one micron (1/25,000 of an inch). This improves the taste of the water used for drinking and preparing food, without adding salt.

Water out of the softener goes to the cold supply line [G] for the rest of the house, including the baths, laundry, dishwasher and so forth. The other side of this tee is the beginning of the water supply to the hot water tank. At this point, a water meter [H] was installed so the water being used during the test period could be measured.

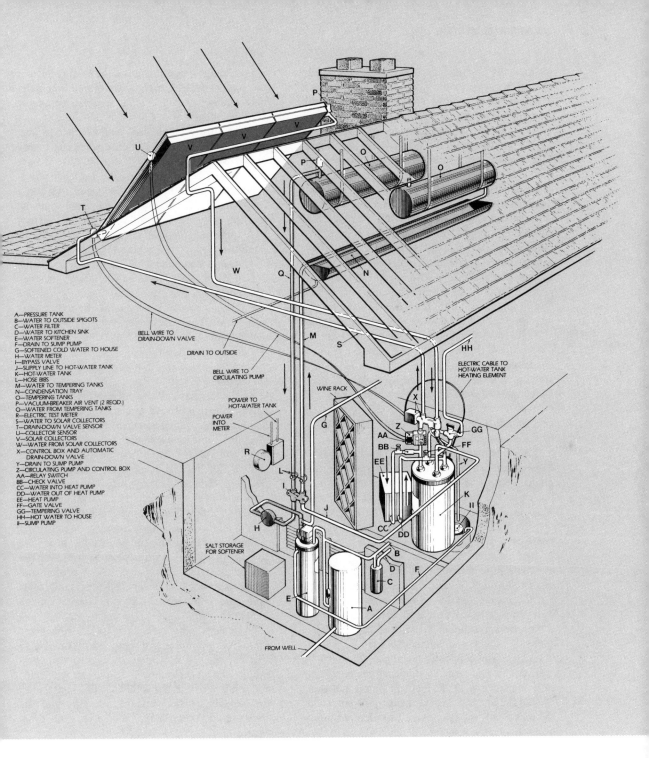

A—PRESSURE TANK
B—WATER TO OUTSIDE SPIGOTS
C—WATER FILTER
D—WATER TO KITCHEN SINK
E—WATER SOFTENER
F—DRAIN TO SUMP PUMP
G—SOFTENED COLD WATER TO HOUSE
H—WATER METER
I—BYPASS VALVE
J—SUPPLY LINE TO HOT-WATER TANK
K—HOT-WATER TANK
L—HOSE BIBS
M—WATER TO TEMPERING TANKS
N—CONDENSATION TRAY
O—TEMPERING TANKS
P—VACUUM-BREAKER AIR VENT (2 REQD.)
Q—WATER FROM TEMPERING TANKS
R—ELECTRIC TEST METER
S—WATER TO SOLAR COLLECTORS
T—DRAIN-DOWN VALVE SENSOR
U—COLLECTOR SENSOR
V—SOLAR COLLECTORS
W—WATER FROM SOLAR COLLECTORS
X—CONTROL BOX AND AUTOMATIC
     DRAIN-DOWN VALVE
Y—DRAIN TO SUMP PUMP
Z—CIRCULATING PUMP AND CONTROL BOX
AA—RELAY SWITCH
BB—CHECK VALVE
CC—WATER INTO HEAT PUMP
DD—WATER OUT OF HEAT PUMP
EE—HEAT PUMP
FF—GATE VALVE
GG—TEMPERING VALVE
HH—HOT WATER TO HOUSE
II—SUMP PUMP

BELL WIRE TO
DRAIN-DOWN VALVE

DRAIN TO OUTSIDE

BELL WIRE TO
CIRCULATING PUMP

POWER TO
HOT-WATER TANK

POWER
INTO
METER

WINE RACK

SALT STORAGE
FOR SOFTENER

FROM WELL

ELECTRIC CABLE TO
HOT-WATER TANK
HEATING ELEMENT

From the meter, the water travels to a specialized bypass valve [I] that diverts it to the tempering tank system. This manual valve is opened or closed, depending on the time of year. During the summer the attic gets extremely hot, often reaching 120° F and higher. Water circulating through the tanks is preheated before it goes to the hot water storage tank. Because the temperature of the well water is a consistent 55° F, using the tempering system makes sense only when the temperature in the attic is consistently (and considerably) higher than 55° F. In locations farther south, its benefits would be greatly increased.

When the temperature falls below the useful point, the valve is moved and the tempering system is bypassed. The tempering system is drained for the year by attaching a garden hose to each hose bib [L]—situated just above the bypass valve—running the hose to the sump pump and opening the valve.

With the tempering tanks out of service, the water goes directly to the storage tank [K], where it enters the top and goes through an internal tube to the bottom of the tank. Near the bottom of this special solar hot water tank is a sensor that monitors the temperature of the entering water. It is connected to another sensor [U]—through the circulating control pump control box [Z]—mounted on the solar collectors on the roof. Together they regulate the circulating pump that supplies the collectors with water. If the temperature of the water inside the tank falls below that of the water inside the collectors, the pump will force the collector water down into the tank.

While two solar collectors will often suffice in other parts of the country, in the northern Illinois test home, three 3 x 8 units were installed. They are angled at 42°, corresponding to the latitude. This angle is a good average for summer solar efficiency. If you are going to use your system all year round, add 5° to the collector angle to compensate for shifts in the sun.

If, at some point, the collectors cannot meet the demand for hot water, then a relay [AA], on the pump control box, will immediately switch power to the heat pump, which will heat the water until the demand subsides. Then the heat pump will kick off and the water will go back to being preheated by the solar collectors.

Keep in mind that when the heat pump is operating, it is drawing heat from the surrounding air. As such, it acts like an air conditioner. For this reason, the device must be installed in a well-ventilated area. If it is placed in a confined room, the surrounding air will quickly become cooled to the point where the heat pump no longer operates efficiently.

If, at any point, the surrounding air temperature drops below 49° F, the heat pump will shut off and the electric resistance heating element in the water tank will take over. This element functions only as a last resort.

Unlike the tempering tanks, the solar collectors do not have to be manually drained when the cold weather arrives. This is handled automatically by means of a drain-down valve [X] that spans both the inflow and outflow lines [S and W] to the collector. The drain-down valve is regulated by another sensor [T] located at the bottom on the bottom side of the roof collectors. When the water temperature inside the panel drops to 45° F, the drain-down valve immediately blocks water from going up to the collectors and drains what is up there down into the sump pump through plastic tubing [Y].

The final component of the system is a tempering valve [GG], installed for safety. This device automatically mixes colder water with the hot water before it goes out of the system for home use. The valve operates only when the water heated by the solar collectors, on the hottest days, is too hot to use.

System costs

Both the solar-collector system and the tempering system will save money when it comes to heating water, but don't expect a quick return on your investment, especially with the collector panels and solar tank. When this system was installed, the Federal Renewable Energy Source tax credit did change the investment picture substantially. It allowed a tax credit of 40 percent of the first $10,000 spent on materials and labor for a solar energy installation.

Another way to ease the financial burden is to stretch out your solar investment by installing the system in stages: first the heat pump, then the tempering tanks or solar collectors and solar tank, and ultimately the pipe insulation on the hot water lines.

No matter what you plan to do, remember there is no guarantee that these federal tax credits will be renewed by Congress. By far, your best money-saving technique is to do the whole installation yourself. By following the installation instructions for the products you buy and the basics of good plumbing, you can cut costs drastically.

Stained glass

■ ESSENTIALLY, A STAINED-GLASS WIN-DOW is a transparent design of colored glass held together by lead strips and enclosed in a frame of wood or metal. Its design can be as complex as a jigsaw puzzle or as simple as a checkerboard.

The latter project can consist of three rows of glass panes, each measuring 2⅞x5½ in. with alternating colors of blue and amber, surrounded by a 1-in.-wide amber border. Tools required are a glass cutter, lead knife, hammer, shingle nails, square, 40 to 80-watt soldering iron, 60-40 solid-core solder and oleic acid (flux).

An inexpensive glass cutter with a steel cutting wheel is adequate for general cutting but one with a tungsten wheel will stay sharp longer. An inexpensive lead knife can be made by sharpening the opposite curve of a linoleum knife. Do not use a soldering iron of higher than recommended wattage or it may melt the lead during soldering.

Cathedral glass is machine-rolled, smooth on one side and has medium to heavy texture on the other. Of uniform ⅛-in. thickness, cathedral glass is cut on the smooth side.

Antique glass is not an old glass, but a product of modern glass chemistry. A very soft glass, it cuts easily on the smooth side.

It's the irregularities of stained glass that enable it to refract and multiply light. In window and door installations, the smooth side of the glass faces inward.

Specially contoured strips of lead, called lead *came,* make up the skeletal component into which stained glass is fitted to compose a stained-glass window. Lead comes in 6-foot strips and must be stretched before cutting to remove crimps and twists. To straighten lead, fasten one end in a vise and grip the other with pliers and pull. A strip will increase about two inches in length after straightening, but avoid excessive stretching as it will weaken the lead. In all window and door designs the longest leads should

1. PATTERN for this 12x20-in. window is penciled, then inked with ¹/₁₆-in.-wide felt-tip pen. Inked lines (called "heart" lines) approximate the ¹/₁₆-in. thickness of lead hearts. Shaded double lines are the ⁹/₁₆-in. border lines.

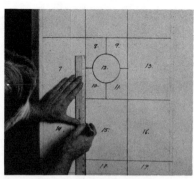

2. WHEN PATTERN IS complex like this one, number each section and corresponding glass pane as they are cut. This is important in a design where several colors of glass are used.

3. TO SCORE GLASS, dip the cu[t] kerosene to clean the cutting whe[el] hold cutter perpendicular to glass begin scoring a fraction of an inch edge of the glass in a continuous stroke without lifting the cutter.

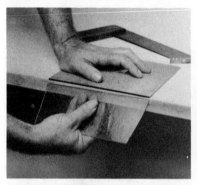

4. AFTER SCORING, place score line parallel to and beyond table edge and press down firmly on each side of line. If score is uniform its full length, glass will separate evenly and cleanly and fit channels of leads perfectly.

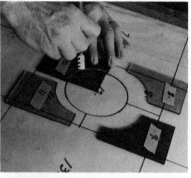

5. WHEN CUTTING out for a rondel, place the glass on top of circle pattern as shown and score glass freehand, carefully following the outside edge of the circular heart line with the cutter. Keep cutter perpendicular to the glass.

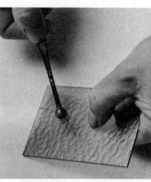

6. TURN THE SCORE line over, the glass as shown, press downw[ard] glass and tap along score line wi[th] ball end of the cutter. As you ger[ntly] tap, you will see glass gradually [frac]ture along the score line.

7. USING YOUR knuckles as a fulcrum, grip the glass with both hands and snap the pane by bending down and outward on both pieces. The glass will part neatly if you make the score line cleanly with the same even pressure.

8. L-SHAPED CLEATS nailed to wood workboard hold the window along two sides and assure squareness. Tap each section of glass firmly into channels of leads with hammer and wood block.

run continuously along the greatest dimension of the design (that is, uncut from border lead to border lead).

The pattern of a leaded-glass window is drawn full-size on white paper and used as a substrate on which the components of the window are assembled. Lay out the pattern first in pencil, then ink the lines with a ⅟₁₆-in.-wide felt-tip pen. The inked lines, called "heart" lines, approximate the ⅟₁₆-in.-thickness of the lead heart on the inside leads.

Staple the pattern to ¾-in.-thick plywood and assemble the window on it. Nail wood cleats at a 90° angle along two sides of the plywood workboard to hold the window components together and insure squareness as the window is assembled. Place three sides of the border lead in position on the pattern, leaving off the fourth side so the glass and inside leads can be fitted into place.

Beginning at the inside corner where cleats intersect, fit a 1-in. border glass into the channels of the border lead and of the inside leads across the width of the window. Now cut the shorter leads that form intersections between the full-length leads and position them across the width of the window, completing the top border. Proceed with the second row of glass and leads, tapping each glass section gently and snugly into place with a hammer and wood block.

Nails hold pieces in place

Use shingle nails across the width of the window and along the border lead to hold the design together. Proceed with the third row of glass and leads. As each glass is fitted into the lead channels, remove the two nails of the preceding row and renail it at the end of the third row. After two or more glass sections have been nailed, soldering can begin.

Solder the two 45° mitered corners of the border leads, then the intersections of the inside leads. To solder an "open" glass section, use scrap glass held with nails to keep solder from running into the channels of open intersections.

After a couple of window sections have been soldered, the remainder of the window is assembled and nailed up to complete the soldering. When all joints and intersections have been sol-

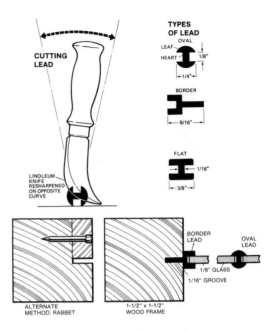

BORDER LEAD is channeled along one edge to fit standard ⅛-in. glass and in section is shaped like a block Y. Flat and oval inside lead is double-channeled and in section is shaped like a capital I.

dered on one side of the design, turn the window over and solder on the opposite side.

Using ⅛-in. solid-core wire solder (rosin-core will not adhere), melt the solder onto the intersection with a tacking motion. Do not preheat the lead intersection as in regular soldering and keep the tip of the iron a fraction of an inch above the lead, dropping the solder onto the lead. If the melted solder "peaks" after soldering, the iron is not hot enough; if the solder bubbles, the iron is too hot. Let the iron cool for a few seconds; then begin again.

Use metal sash putty (gray) to fill gaps in the lead channels. With your thumb, force the putty in between the glass and the lead leaves on both sides of the window.

When puttying is completed, remove putty oils and residue from the oleic acid by scrubbing both sides of the window with dry sawdust and a stiff brush. Let putty set overnight before installing window in its frame.

Stained glass projects made the easy way

■ YOU CAN GIVE the distinctive look of stained glass to your workshop projects with very little effort and no special tools. The modern version, using liquid lead squeezed from a bottle, combined with glass stains applied with eyedroppers, eliminates the time-consuming, exacting techniques of cutting glass and fusing pieces. Yet the effects are comparable in beauty to real stained glass.

To introduce you to this colorful craft, we've designed three shop projects around stained-glass

panels. Following are glass-staining tips.

Wash glass with vinegar

To stain a pane of glass or a mirror, wash it thoroughly with a vinegar-and-water solution or alcohol. For an acrylic panel, first remove the protective paper and wash the plastic with warm water. Dry with a soft, lint-free cloth. Enlarge the pattern to full size.

To stain a mirror or frosted acrylic, transfer the pattern to it with carbon paper. On clear acrylic or glass, place the pattern underneath on a flat surface. Apply liquid lead (black) or liquid pewter (gray) following the pattern lines.

Cut the tip of the liquid lead applicator, taking care not to cut too large a hole. You can enlarge it later if necessary.

Test size of bead

Squeeze the lead onto scrap paper to check the size (diameter) of the bead that is formed. Once the hole size is correct, you can use the top on subsequent bottles. Store it after each project for use on the next one.

Outline the design on the panel with liquid lead, being careful that every bit of the line adheres. Each section must be a tight well so the stains cannot run together. Use a toothpick to dab the bead down where it's not secure. Let the leading dry overnight. Note: Don't expose this water-based material to the outdoors.

Applying the glass stain

Place the outlined piece on a *level* surface so the stain won't flow beyond its enclosure. Apply the stain with eye droppers, using a different dropper for each color.

To avoid accidents, hold a tissue under the dropper until it is directly over the area to be filled. To achieve the best color, fill each area with stain as far as possible, without letting the stain overflow.

If any bubbles should appear during the application, use the dropper to remove them. If you expel as much air as possible from the dropper before inserting it into the stain bottle, the bubbles will be negligible.

CASA LIGHT BOX

Begin work by cutting frame parts (A,B,C) to size. Cut grooves in these parts to hold backing

(G). Also miter the ends and cut grooves for splines (I). Sand these parts smooth.

Cut hardwood splines and assemble the frame with glue and clamps. Check that it is square; let the glue dry overnight. Next day, secure with well-set 6d finishing nails at joints. Fill holes with wood filler.

Install cleats

Cut and temporarily install cleats (E,F). These are removed later for painting. Bore vent holes at top and bottom. Cut and test-fit back (G).

Rip a length of 1⅛-in. round to suit for molding (D). Sand smooth.

Temporarily install panel (H) and tack-nail molding (D) to check fit. Note: If your decorative panel is sheet acrylic, allow expansion space when installing molding and cleats to prevent stress. Install hardware at back. Check parts for fit and disassemble.

Install lamps

Install the fluorescent lamps, making the connections as shown in the drawing. Carefully locate lamps (J) to allow clearance between them and the front and back panels. Cut the lamp wires to length *after* fixtures are in place. Make the splices as shown and secure them with solderless connectors (M). The connectors, canopy switch (L) and extra lamp wire are hardware and lamp-store items. After testing, remove the fixtures from the box. Permanently secure molding (D) to the frame with 1-in. brads (two per strip), and use wood filler in holes.

Apply sealer

Sand again if needed. Dust and wipe with a tack rag. Apply a coat of sealer (pigmented shellac) and let dry overnight. Sand lightly, dust and wipe with a tack rag. Apply paint, covering the inside, too, to aid reflectivity. Paint cleats (E,F) out of the box. They are easier to paint that way.

When parts are dry, lay the box face down and reassemble in this order: Install Casa panel. Install cleats (E,F) using ¾-in. brads. Install the lamps and arrange the wires around the frame. Keep them in place with insulated staples, being careful that the staples don't penetrate the insulation.

Install the back, remount the hardware and hang the unit from a pair of hefty picture hangers. Note that lower screw eyes (O) act as spacers to keep the box parallel with the wall; otherwise it would hang at an angle.

EACH SQ. = 2"

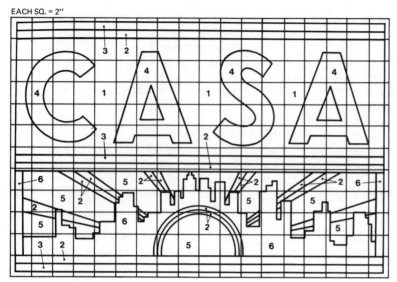

MATERIALS LIST—CASA LIGHT BOX

Key	No.	Size and description (use)
A	2	¾ × 3⅜ × 25⁹/₁₆" pine (sides)
B	1	¾ × 3⅜ × 37⁹/₁₆" pine (bottom)
C	1	¾ × 3 × 37⁹/₁₆" pine (top)
D	1	1⅛"-dia. × 11' round; cut 4 pieces to size (molding)
E	2	¼ × ¼ × 36" pine (top, bottom cleats)
F	1	¼ × ¼ × 23½" pine (side cleat)
G	1	⅛ × 24½ × 36½" hardboard (back)
H	1	¼ × 24 × 36" opal/frosted acrylic (glass stain panel)
I	4	⅛ × ½ × 4" hardwood (spline)
J	2	24" Bright Stik (light)
K	2	L-hook (back fastener)
L	1	canopy switch
M	3	solderless connector
N	1	power cord and plug (with Bright Stik)
O	4	medium-size screw eye (for hanging)
P	1	55" picture-hanging wire.

Misc.: 1" brads; ¾" brads; lamp wire; 6d finishing nails; wood filler; white glue; pigmented shellac and glossy white paint. To stain the panel, you'll need eye droppers; full-size pattern; toothpick; four 4-oz. bottles of Titan's Liquid Lead. Also, 2-oz. bottles of Glas Stain in the following colors: Royal Blue, 2 bottles (1)*; Hot Orange, 1 bottle (2); Red, 1 bottle (3); Lemon, 2 bottles (4); White, 2 bottles (5); and Black, 1 bottle (6).
*Numbers in parenthesis match color code in pattern, left.

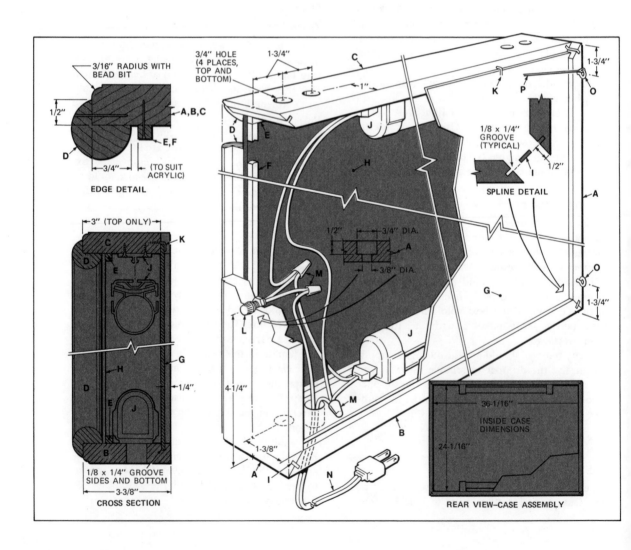

RAGONFLY in brilliant blues pre-
s over this glass-stained mirror. The
dsome frame, made from conven-
al wooden moldings, is an original
gn from our workshop.

DRAGONFLY MIRROR

Start work on the mirror frame by cutting base frame (A). Sand, and then cut the frame molding (B), beginning with the inside pieces. These four pieces overhang the inside of the base frame by ¼ in. and form the rabbet that holds the mirror (E). Measure carefully and cut the miters on the inside molding pieces so that they are ½ in. less than the length and width of the base cutout. This creates the glass-holding rabbet. Attach with glue.

Attach molding

Measure, cut and attach the remaining molding pieces (B,C) using glue and 1¼-in. brads. Set brads slightly and fill holes with wood filler. Temporarily position the completed dragonfly mirror. Cut and test-fit molding (D); then remove mirror.

Sand the frame, if needed, before finishing it. Dust and wipe with a tack cloth. Apply two coats of satin varnish as directed, sanding, dusting and wiping with a tack cloth between coats. Reinstall mirror and back molding. Attach screw eyes (F) and picture wire (G).

PRACTICE on scrap until you can apply liquid lead in a uniform line.

PLACE full-size pattern under the panel; trace the lines with liquid lead.

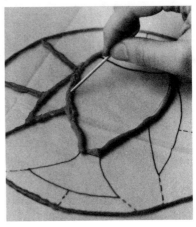

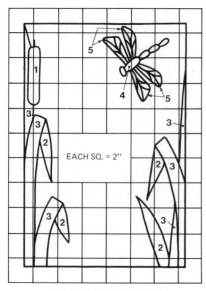

EACH SQ. = 2''

MATERIALS LIST—MIRROR

Key	No.	Size and description (use)
A	1	¾ × 20 × 26" plywood (frame base)
B	1	⁹/₁₆ × 1⅛" × 24' half round, cut to size (molding)
C	1	⅜ × ¾" by 8' half round; cut to size (edging)
D	1	½ × ½" × 8' quarter round, cut to size (back molding)
E	1	¼ × 14¼ × 20⅛" mirror (decorative panel)
F	2	small-size screw eye (for hanging)
G	1	30" picture-hanging wire

Misc.: ¾'' brads; 1¼'' brads; white glue; wood filler and varnish. To glass-stain the mirror, you'll need: eye droppers; carbon paper; full-size pattern; pencil; toothpick; one 4-oz. bottle of Titan's Liquid Lead. Also, one 2-oz. bottle of Glas Stain in each of the following colors: Amber (1)*, Lime (2), Emerald (3), Turquoise (4), Light Blue (5).
* Numbers in parentheses match color code in pattern above.

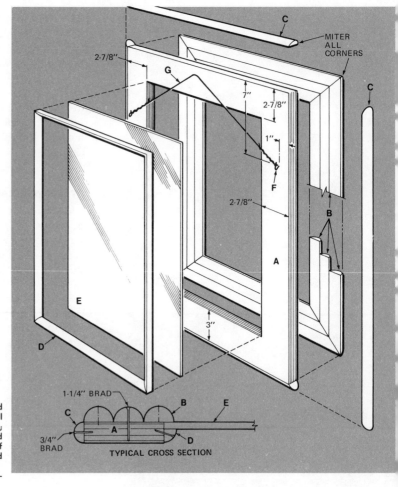

PRESS DOWN on the lead with a toothpick so all areas adhere to panel.

APPLY GLASS STAIN with eyedroppers. Hold tissue under dropper.

YOU CAN SECTION off living space and still maintain an open feeling with this colorful zodiac panel. To separate areas, suspend the panel over a bookcase.

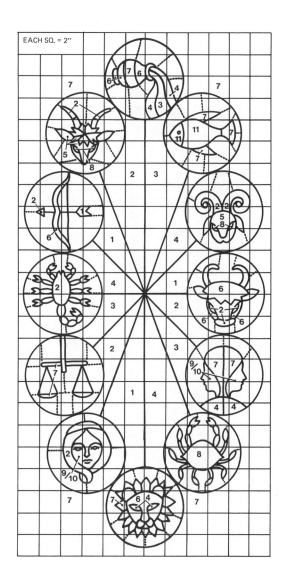

EACH SQ. = 2″

ZODIAC HANGING DIVIDER

When you stain the zodiac panel, be certain that the edges of the circles are touching so that the background yellow doesn't flow into the center. Spindles (A,B,C) are ready-made and available at many lumberyards.

Rip four strips of hardwood (E,F) for the frame. Cut a ³⁄₁₆x¼-in.-deep groove down the centers to hold the zodiac panel. Note: Acrylic expands and contracts, so make sure the panel is loose in the grooves to prevent stress.

Cut the cross members

Cut the shaped upper and lower cross members (D) with a band or sabre saw. Sand the ripples smooth. Mortise recesses in D to receive sides (E). Bevel edges of D using a router with 45° bevel cutter.

Test-fit the frame parts with the zodiac panel in place. Nail and glue parts (F) in place. Trim spindles (C) to fit the assembly. Mark them before cutting so you can produce an accurate fit.

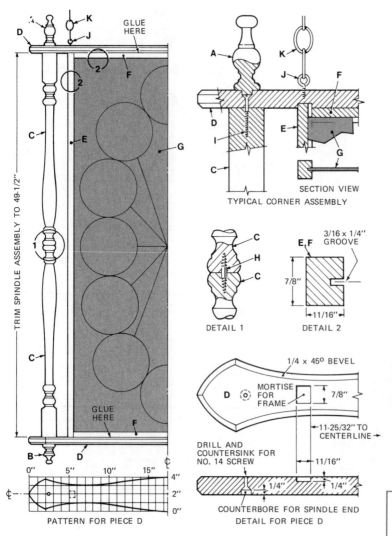

TRIM SPINDLE ASSEMBLY TO 49-1/2"

GLUE HERE

GLUE HERE

TYPICAL CORNER ASSEMBLY

SECTION VIEW

DETAIL 1

DETAIL 2

3/16 x 1/4" GROOVE

7/8"

11/16"

PATTERN FOR PIECE D

1/4 x 45° BEVEL

MORTISE FOR FRAME

7/8"

11-25/32" TO CENTERLINE

DRILL AND COUNTERSINK FOR NO. 14 SCREW

11/16"

1/4"   1/4"

COUNTERBORE FOR SPINDLE END
DETAIL FOR PIECE D

MAKE MORTISES in the cross members (D) by first boring ¼ x ¾-in.-dia. holes to remove much of the waste. Chisel out remaining waste to the bottom of the hole.

TRIM oversize spindles (C) to fit. Use a straightedge or square to mark cut.

Clamp spindles

Clamp the spindles in place with bar clamps. Bore pilot holes for attachment screws through cross members (D) into the long spindles. Counterbore for the screwheads.

Assemble the unit without the zodiac panel. Attach screw eyes (J) and chain (K); hang to paint. Finish end spindles separately. Disassemble, keeping mating parts together; reassemble with panel.

MATERIALS LIST—ZODIAC PANEL

Key	No.	Size and description (use)
A	2	large spindle end
B	2	small spindle end
C	4	30" stock spindle turning or two 60" turnings
D	2	¹³⁄₁₆ x 4 x 35" maple (cross member)
E	2	¹¹⁄₁₆ x ⅞ x 49½" maple (vertical frame)
F	2	¹¹⁄₁₆ x ⅞ x 29³⁄₁₆" maple (horizontal frame)
G	1	⅛ x 24 x 48" acrylic sheet (decorative panel)
H	2	dowel screw
I	4	2" No. 14 fh screw
J	2	large-size screw eye
K	2	chain as needed to suspend panel

Misc.: White glue and black semigloss spray paint. To glass-stain the panel, you'll need: full-size pattern; eye droppers; toothpick; four or five 4-oz. bottles of Titan's Liquid Pewter or Liquid Lead. Also, 2-oz. bottles of Glas Stain in the following colors: Red, 2 bottles (1)*; Amber, 2 bottles (2); Light Blue, 2 bottles (3); Turquoise, 2 bottles (4); White, 1 bottle (5); Yellow, 1 bottle (6); Lemon Yellow, 2 or 3 bottles (7); Pumpkin, 1 bottle (8); Pink, 1 bottle (9); Clear Extender, 1 bottle (10); and Hot Orange, 1 bottle (11).

Lay out and build your own stairs

■ CHANCES ARE, the stairs a homeowner is most likely to replace are either in the basement or on the back porch. Interior stairs are generally of the more intricate housed-stringer type (below). This type should be left to professional stairbuilders.

You can build stairs either in your shop or at their location. Generally speaking, the more intricate the stair design, the better it is to do the building in the shop. But if you do, make certain you will be able to move the finished staircase into its position.

Three things to keep in mind when laying out and installing a stairway are safety, adequate headroom and space for the passage of furniture. If the stair rise is too steep or too shallow, the steps are sure to be difficult to ascend and descend, and could cause missteps and falls. Poor layout may result in inadequate headroom which could lead to bumped heads (for tall persons) and inability to maneuver furniture up or down the stairs.

In most homes, there are two types of stairs. Principal stairs are designed to provide easy, comfortable access to another level; they are architecturally coordinated to the room in which they are located. The second type, service (or basement) stairs, are generally steeper and constructed of less expensive materials.

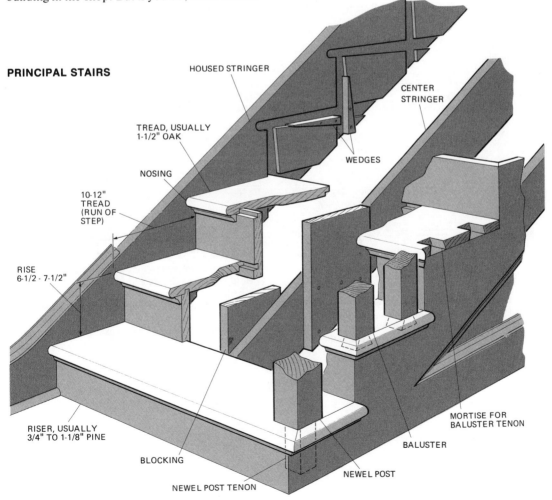

PRINCIPAL STAIRS

HOUSED STRINGER

CENTER STRINGER

TREAD, USUALLY 1-1/2" OAK

WEDGES

NOSING

10-12" TREAD (RUN OF STEP)

RISE 6-1/2 - 7-1/2"

MORTISE FOR BALUSTER TENON

RISER, USUALLY 3/4" TO 1-1/8" PINE

BALUSTER

BLOCKING

NEWEL POST

NEWEL POST TENON

TYPES OF STAIRS

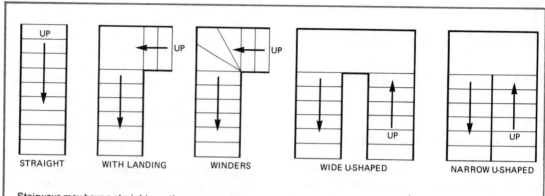

STRAIGHT   WITH LANDING   WINDERS   WIDE U-SHAPED   NARROW U-SHAPED

Stairways may have a straight, continuous run with or without an intermediate platform (landing), or they can consist of two or more runs at angles to each other. If your stairs must have an angle, it is at this point that the landing should be installed.

Another stair design incorporates winders—the turn is negotiated by radiating treads. For safety, if winders must be used, they should be installed at, or near the foot—not at the top—of the stairs.

Remember these points when laying out stairs:
1. Allow for minimum headroom of 80 in.
2. Generally, treads should be between 10 and 12 in. wide and risers should be 7½-in. high. The formula used by most professionals is: Twice the riser height plugs the tread width should equal 25. When you lay out your stairs, use risers that will put you close to that number.
3. Angle of the stairs should be between 30° and 36°.

STAIRWAY DESIGN

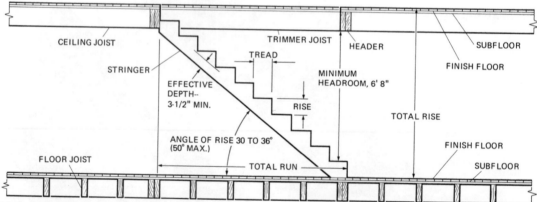

There is a definite relationship between width of treads and height of riser. All stairs should be laid out to conform with these well-established rules.

Any variance from these standards will result in awkward stairs which create a safety hazard and are tiring to use. If the treads are too short, the risers will be too high, so that your toe is likely to kick the riser on each step. But when the treads are too long, the risers will be too low,

enough so that you will be making a conscientious effort to shorten your stride; this, too, is tiring.

Experience has proven that a riser of 7 to 7½ in. is about perfect. By using the formula mentioned you will find that the tread for a 7½-in. riser is 10 in. For comfort, as the riser gets shorter, the tread should be correspondingly wider. For example, a 6½-in. riser should have a 12-in. tread.

MATHEMATICS IN STAIRBUILDING

When replacing an existing stairway, you already know its location and width, but you will need to determine the correct height of the risers and width of the treads. (If a landing is to be included, consider it—for design purposes—as simply another step. Its length and width will be decided by the available space at the landing location.)

To figure the number of riser needed, you first select a suitable riser height. Then divide the total rise—distance in inches from top of the lower floor to top of the upper floor—by the riser height chosen.

If you get a full number as your answer, let it represent the amount of risers needed. Usually, however, the result will include a fraction. When this happens, divide the story (total) height by the whole number that's nearest (above or below) the fractional answer. The result of this second division will give the riser height. You can then proportion the tread by using the formula outlined on the preceding page.

In another formula to adjust riser height, you multiply the tread width by the riser height. Ideally, the answer should be as close to 75 as possible. Thus, a riser height of $7\frac{1}{2}$ in. multiplied by a tread width of 10 in. gives the perfect combination—75.

Here's an example of such calculations, assuming a story height of 9 ft. 6 in., or 114 in. and riser height of $7\frac{1}{2}$ in. When you divide the 114-in. story height by $7\frac{1}{2}$ in., you get $15\text{-}\frac{1}{5}$ risers. Obviously, you cannot have a fifth of a riser, so the nearest whole number to use in the next calculation is 15. In other words, you can assume that 15 risers will be required, so you now divide the total story height of 114 in. by 15 in. to get 7.6 in., or approximately $7\frac{9}{16}$ in. as the height for each riser.

Next, to find the width of the treads, multiply the riser height by 2 and subtract this from 25. For example, $2 \times 7\frac{9}{16}$ in. equals $15\frac{1}{8}$ in. Deduct this figure from 25, which leave $9\frac{7}{8}$ in. as the correct tread width.

Thus, the figures you should use for this example stairway are:

1. Risers: 15, each $7\frac{9}{16}$ in. high.
2. Treads: 14, each $9\frac{7}{8}$ in. wide.

Note that there is always one more riser than the number of treads.

TYPES OF STRINGER (CARRIAGES)

PLANNING STRINGERS

Treads and risers should be fixed solidly to stringers that are set level and plumb. Several methods for fastening treads and risers to stringers are shown above. Stringers shown here can be built by a careful do-it-yourselfer. The intricate housed stringer with tapered dadoes and wedges is better left in the hands of a pro.

In contemporary architecture, open stairways are frequently called for; that is, no risers are used. This type of stairway is becoming increasingly popular as modern architecture comes into greater use. However, when you contemplate replacing a stairway in an older home, the stair design should remain conventional—unless the entire home decor is being changed—in order to conform to the house style. It's safe to say that in a majority of cases a stairway should be replaced by a design that is similar to that of the original stairway.

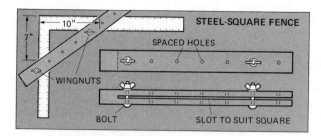

STEEL-SQUARE FENCE

SPACED HOLES

WINGNUTS

BOLT SLOT TO SUIT SQUARE

FOR ACCURACY, USE A FENCE

It is just about impossible to lay out a stringer accurately without an aid such as the fence shown at left. Use hardwood and simply bore a series of in-line holes down the center of the fence to accommodate a pair of wingnuts. Then, saw a slot through from the top to the bottom so that the fence can be used on the square as shown.

LAYING OUT A STRINGER

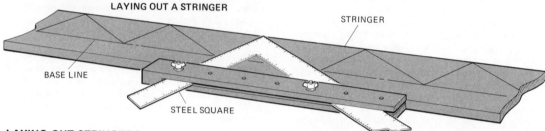

STRINGER

BASE LINE

STEEL SQUARE

LAYING OUT STRINGERS

Since lumber shrinkage is one of the stairbuilder's worst enemies, you will be wise to use only well-seasoned lumber. If you plan to construct a principal stairway, you can purchase treads and risers of standard widths from a local lumberyard. Most yards also stock (or can quickly get) standard oak treads that are dressed to an actual thickness of $1^1/_{16}$ in. These days it is not uncommon to find risers constructed of 1-in. pine (actual dimension, ¾ in.). But since there is less chance of cupping and warpage with the heftier stock, you'll find it better to use 1⅛-in. material (5/4-in. stock).

Starting steps (with curved ends), newel posts, handrails and balusters also are stock items carried by most building-supply outlets.

Secondary stairs are generally built using 2x6, 2x8 or 2x10 lumber for the stringers and treads. If risers are to be installed on such a stairway, they can be of ¾-in. stock.

After calculating the number of risers and treads required, and their respective height and width, begin by laying them out on the stringers as shown in the above sketch using a steel framing square. Your layout must be accurate.

After riser and tread positions have been indicated on the stringers, you can proceed with construction of the stairs. Stringers can be cleated, dadoed or notched, depending on your preference. If they are of the latter type, for structural reasons you must adhere to the 3½-in. minimum distance between base line and edge of stringer as shown in the drawing.

If stringers are to be dadoed, construct a template or jig from ¼-in. plywood which can be clamped or tacked to the stringers to guide your router. When you're satisfied that the jig is accurate, make match marks on it so that it can be aligned accurately on the stringer each time it is relocated. The jig design should allow at least one riser and one tread groove to be made with each clamped setup.

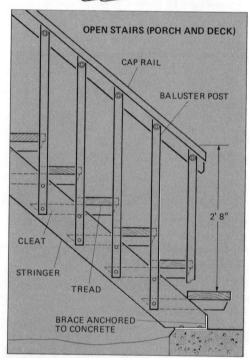

OPEN STAIRS (PORCH AND DECK)

CAP RAIL

BALUSTER POST

2' 8"

CLEAT

STRINGER

TREAD

BRACE ANCHORED TO CONCRETE

ABOUT HANDRAILS

For safety—particularly for the elderly—all stairways should have a handrail. On a closed stairway, it is simply attached to the wall using handrail brackets. On open stairs, the handrail is located atop balusters which end against a newel post at the foot of the stairs. Usually balusters are dovetailed into the treads, but they can be installed by toenailing three or four finishing nails into the tread. If you use the latter method, predrill pilot holes to prevent splitting the hardwood treads. Regardless of stair style, handrails should always be 32 in. above the tread at the riser line.

Brick and masonry steps

■ EXTERIOR STAIRS should be designed and built as carefully as interior stairs. Their riser-to-tread ratios vary somewhat from interior-stair standards: Riser height on principal exterior stairs should be between 6 and 7 in., with a minimum tread of 12 in. In most outdoor situations, you'll have room to meet these specifications without going through complicated calculations. Good support for the weight of materials is essential to make steps that will be stable and won't crack through settling. If located over backfill, their footings must rest on undisturbed ground.

Common (building) bricks come in many colors and three grades; unless frost is extremely infrequent in your area, SW, for severe weathering, is the grade you'll want. Used brick is attractive in many applications, but it is necessary to check each individual brick for cracks. Even the smallest cracks can open up and cause problems. What comes closest to a standard size for common brick is 2¾ x 4½ x 8½ in. nominal. Actual size is ½ in. smaller in each dimension—the space taken up by ½-in. mortar joints between bricks. By using the nominal size in estimating the number of bricks needed, you get an automatic allowance for joint space—but check on the sizes stocked locally before estimating. Otherwise you may waste your time on computations and then find that what you need is not in stock at your supplier.

The space between your finished steps and house foundation must be sealed to prevent moisture from entering this area. This is done by filling the joint with oakum (a fibrous material), then applying tar or mortar caulk.

Bonds, mortar and joints

Rowlock steps and header steps are the two basic brick-step bonds. Either can be laid with slight nosing (overlap of tread); this should not exceed ½ in. Note that foundation for header steps in other drawings is simpler. Type M (high-strength) mortar should be used according to directions; mix only what you can use in 2½ hours. Mortar can be colored with lampblack or pigments. Work from the bottom up, laying bricks on a ⅜-in. mortar bed and checking with a level as you go. Flush mortar joints made with trowel edge will weather best. When mortar has set, rub with a clean brick to remove excess.

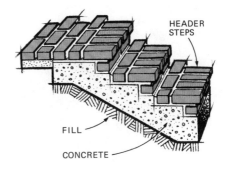

HEADER STEPS

FILL

CONCRETE

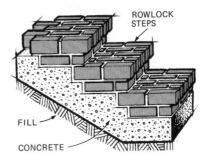

ROWLOCK STEPS

FILL

CONCRETE

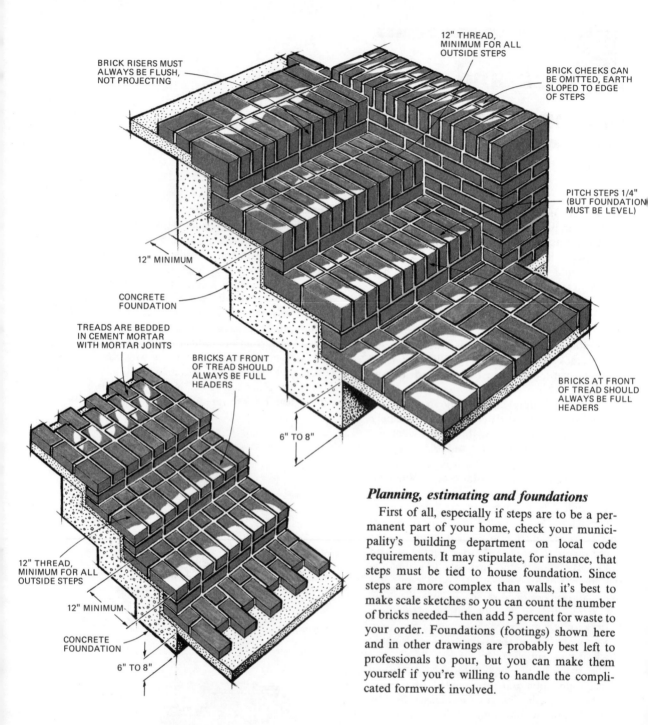

12" THREAD, MINIMUM FOR ALL OUTSIDE STEPS

BRICK RISERS MUST ALWAYS BE FLUSH, NOT PROJECTING

BRICK CHEEKS CAN BE OMITTED, EARTH SLOPED TO EDGE OF STEPS

PITCH STEPS 1/4" (BUT FOUNDATION MUST BE LEVEL)

12" MINIMUM

CONCRETE FOUNDATION

TREADS ARE BEDDED IN CEMENT MORTAR WITH MORTAR JOINTS

BRICKS AT FRONT OF TREAD SHOULD ALWAYS BE FULL HEADERS

6" TO 8"

BRICKS AT FRONT OF TREAD SHOULD ALWAYS BE FULL HEADERS

12" THREAD, MINIMUM FOR ALL OUTSIDE STEPS

12" MINIMUM

CONCRETE FOUNDATION

6" TO 8"

Planning, estimating and foundations

First of all, especially if steps are to be a permanent part of your home, check your municipality's building department on local code requirements. It may stipulate, for instance, that steps must be tied to house foundation. Since steps are more complex than walls, it's best to make scale sketches so you can count the number of bricks needed—then add 5 percent for waste to your order. Foundations (footings) shown here and in other drawings are probably best left to professionals to pour, but you can make them yourself if you're willing to handle the complicated formwork involved.

Formwork, pouring, finishing for concrete steps

Footings for concrete steps should be below the area frost line and at least 8 in. thick. When the footing has set, a concrete-block foundation wall can be built up to grade with blocks mortared together and their cores filled with mortar. After the mortar has set (about 24 hours), backfill the soil around the wall, carefully tamping each 6-in. layer, until tamped backfill is at grade. The site is now ready for forms, which should be built as shown above with ¾-in. plywood for batter boards and 1-in. and 2-in. nominal stock for bracing. Forms must be well nailed and solid, so that pressure of concrete will not force them apart.

Since steps of this type require a large amount of concrete, you are well advised to use transit-mix (truck-mixed) concrete, pouring the steps monolithically (as a single unit); the stiffness of the mix should make it unnecessary to close in lower-step treads. You *can* hand-mix and pour one layer at a time, but this is not really worth the extra effort, as it raises the problem of tying the layers together. Estimate the amount of concrete needed by finding the volume of the steps in cubic feet and dividing by 27 to convert to cubic yards, and add 5 percent for waste. One cu. yd. is usually the minimum order for transit-mix concrete. Before pouring, give the inside of the forms a thin coat of form oil to keep concrete from adhering to wood. When the pour is complete, rap forms vigorously all over with a hammer; this helps the mix to settle and fill voids (honeycombs) that may occur next to the form boards. You should *not* pour if the temperature is below 40° F or if it is raining. Use a wood float to finish the steps—a steel trowel would give too slick a surface. When concrete has set for at least 36 hours, carefully remove forms. Rough spots can be rubbed smooth with a Carborundum stone and water. Fill any voids at this time with a cement-and-sand mix, troweled and rubbed smooth with the stone while still wet. To cure, keep steps moist and covered (to retain moisture) for five to seven days.

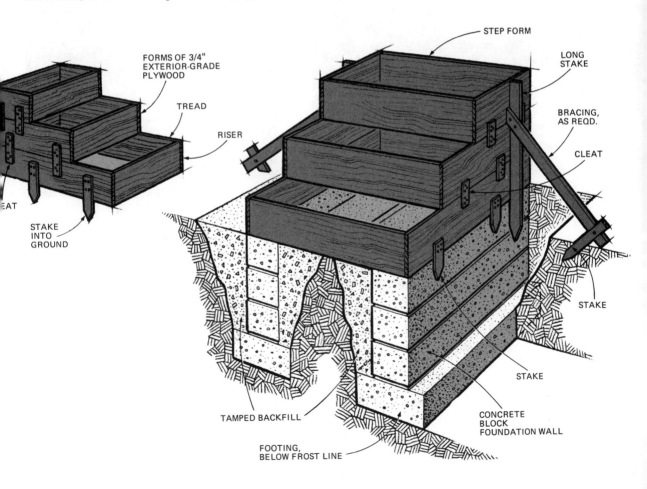

FORMS OF 3/4"
EXTERIOR-GRADE
PLYWOOD

TREAD

RISER

CLEAT

STAKE
INTO
GROUND

STEP FORM

LONG
STAKE

BRACING,
AS REQD.

CLEAT

STAKE

STAKE

TAMPED BACKFILL

CONCRETE
BLOCK
FOUNDATION WALL

FOOTING,
BELOW FROST LINE

AFTER THE DOOR FRAME is placed in position, the siding is marked along the top to determine where to cut.

THE ENTRY IS positioned and fastened to the new foundation; the joint is dressed with mortar.

THE CONCRETE is allowed to set before you engage torsion bars in clips attached to the entry sidepieces.

THE PITCHED CONCRETE ledge gives positive water run-off and makes lawn-trimming a lot easier.

Stairwell to your basement

■ ANYONE WITH A BASEMENT WORK-SHOP can quickly count off the advantages to be gained by installing an outside—direct-access—basement entry such as the one shown below. By adding this convenience to your basement you can:

● Haul lumber down to your shop effortlessly, even when the materials include 4 x 8 sheets of plywood.

● Tackle almost any project because you won't find yourself—as cartoonists like to depict, for example—with a completed boat in the basement instead of in the water.

● Quickly store large items such as patio furniture and storm windows in the basement where you can work on them in comfort during the off-season.

From the family viewpoint, direct access is especially important if you have a swimming pool or basement playroom. Related equipment and furnishings can then be toted in or out without any traffic through first-floor rooms. And, perhaps most important, direct-access will give you a fast route to safety should an emergency arise.

Aside from the obvious advantages of a steel installation (termite protection and minimum maintenance), the doors shown offer an additional good feature: When a particularly heavy or bulky item must be moved in or out of the basement, treads can be quickly removed so the object can be passed through easily.

Location of the entrance is important. If possible, it should go where the outside grade is lowest. This cuts down on the materials needed as well as the number of steps you will have to climb. And, of course, make certain that the finished grade slopes away for proper drainage.

Dig the hole large enough to take the new foundation plus an extra foot all around to allow for waterproofing and the footing. It is best to do the digging in stages, cutting the foundation as you go. This permits safer and easier handling of the cutting tool.

Electrical tools for cutting through a poured foundation can be rented from a local mason supply house or tool-rental outlet to speed up this step. A good tool for the job is a rotary hammer, which both rotates and hammers, and comes with a variety of bits. The chisel attachment, for example, will remove large sections with less rubble. If you have a concrete block foundation, cutting will be easier.

After excavating and breaking through the foundation, a 12-in. concrete footing goes in to provide a firm, level base for the first course of block. Simply dig a 12-in.-wide trench 4 in. deep

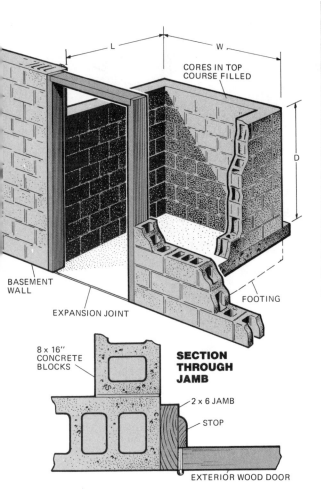

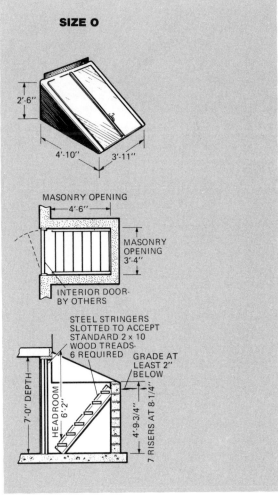

and pour the footing without forms. The top course of block should be about 4 in. above ground. After stuffing the hollow-block cores with heavy paper, trowel on a concrete cap and insert anchors as required.

Assembling the doors in place will save work. Here, make certain that the caulking strips provided are inserted between the header and sidepieces. Installation is not difficult if you read and follow the instructions packed with the doors. It's a must to follow them closely in order to validate the maker's guarantee of a weather-tight door.

ALL HARDWARE, including steel step-stringers, comes with the doors. The owner supplies 2x10s for the treads.

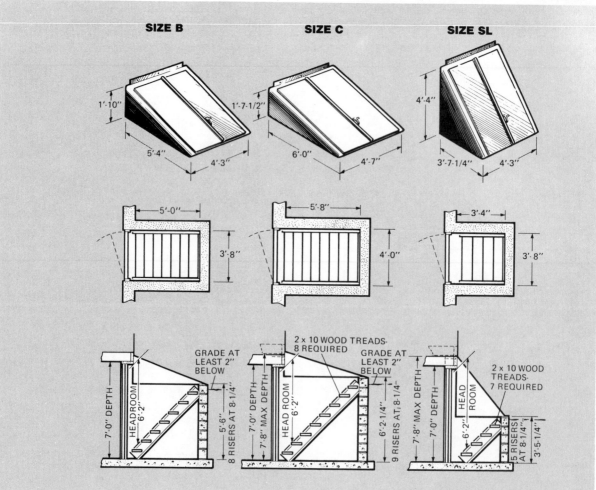

SIZE B

SIZE C

SIZE SL

Record care: it pays to be tender

■ RECORD CARE has grown from a small industry selling mainly treated cloths to giant companies using space-age technology to guard discs against nicks, scratches and static. Along with the new ways to take care of records has come quite a bit of confusion over which method is best for which problem. There's even some question about how some of the more esoteric products work. You'll have to make your own judgment as to which system works best for your particular situation.

Preventive maintenance

The most common form of record care doesn't cost a penny. Store your records properly (on edge, packed firmly together but not tightly squeezed), and be sure to put them back in their dust jackets as soon as you've played them. Take care never to touch the recorded grooves—your fingertip oils will glue down airborne dust.

A dust cover for your turntable will keep records from getting dirtier while you play them and will slow down the rate at which the turntable collects dust it can transfer to records later.

For cleaning records, there are a variety of products now on the market.

Disc cleaning pads

Perhaps the best known device is a directionally textured plush pad mounted on a wood handle. The pad is wetted with a special solution and drawn around the record, tracking the grooves. As you brush the record, dust is swept up into the soft pad.

Variations in this product include the liquid used to loosen the dirt, which can range from water to multichemical and antistatic formulas.

Buffing lubricants

While most of the devices on the market have some sort of fluid to aid them, the basic item is really the wiper or brush. There is, however, a group of products for which the reverse is true. You still squirt or spray a product onto a record or pad, but you *buff* the substance rather than wipe up the dirt. The application is more important than the applicator.

One of these space-age technology products forms a chemical bond with the vinyl groove and locks out dirt and grit; it also acts as a lubricant to reduce the friction of the stylus in the groove.

Other pump-spray products contain not only a preservative/lubricant but a cleaner and antistatic agent as well.

Ionic neutralizers

If you find you have lots of pops and clicks (symptomatic of static electricity) on your discs, you may want to try one of the solely antistatic products on the market. These are usually pistol-shaped products. A slow squeeze of the trigger over the disc and static-neutralizing ions are released over the records. These products do, however, produce a voltage and carry warnings not to aim at people and to keep out of the reach of children.

Antistatic sleeves and mats

Once you've taken the trouble to remove static from your disc's surface, you will want to keep the static charge down with antistatic felt-type mats.

Antistatic record jackets protect against the static charge that can be created simply by removing a disc from its sleeve. Some of these are all plastic; others feature a paper sleeve with a plastic lining.

Facials and vacuums

Some products can give the surface and grooves of your records a deep cleaning the same way a standard facial removes dirt and oil from the skin. The application is similar, too. Just

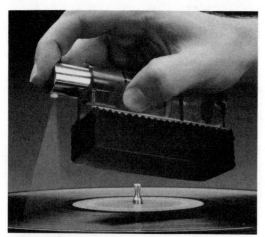

WHILE THE BASIC cleaning agent is the brush or pad, some record cleaners also use a spray to help.

THE MOST BASIC record cleaner uses a brush to wipe dust. This model has conductive bristles to avoid static.

ANOTHER VARIATION has bristles in the center to loosen dust and plush ends to pick dust up.

THIS MODEL has a directionally textured pad and a pocket to hold the solution bottle.

THIS LUBRICANT-TYPE cleaner is moistened by an internal wick.

THIS DRY LUBRICANT forms a chemical bond with the vinyl groove to lock out dirt and grit.

squirt the goo on the record and wait (usually about 45 minutes to an hour) and then peel the hardened film from the disc. Along with the preparation should come all the dust, dirt and grime you've let accumulate.

If the hour wait is too long for you, try vacuum-cleaning your records before you play them. One model looks a little like a shark's jaw. You place the record in the groove (the shark's mouth) and turn on the machine, and the record is rotated and both sides are vacuumed clean.

Cleaning the stylus

Your stylus should be kept clean and your turntable level. A clean stylus will not push and grind dirt into the grooves of a clean record. A level turntable won't turn your diamond stylus into a Grade-A cutting tool. One stylus cleaner is a soft pad mounted on clear plastic. Another offers a brush on one side and a magnifying mirror on the other. A kit with a brush, small screwdriver (for cartridge hardware), stylus microscope and cleaning fluid is also available.

Stabilizers

The most unusual devices are the stabilizers. Available from several companies, these heavyweights are designed to fit over the label area of your record and on the spindle. Many records arrive already warped, and the heavy weight will tend to flatten them for the time they are on the turntable, at least.

UNDER THE MICROSCOPE, you can see thin shavings worn by even a fresh stylus accounting for some of the fuzz that gathers on the stylus.

A lubricated stylus appears fuzz-free. The grooves on the record shown average 0.003 in. in width.

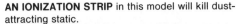

AN IONIZATION STRIP in this model will kill dust-attracting static.

THIS ANTISTATIC GUN generates ions as you squeeze the trigger over the record.

Compact disc players

■ THE DRAWER GLIDES OPEN without a sound, inviting you to drop in your latest laser disc. It slides closed just as quietly, and the disc spins up to speed. You can then listen to the music without lifting a finger, or you can take over, playing the panel controls to pick off the disc just what you want to hear. Select any track with the touch of a button, skim through all the selections, hearing a snippet of each; or punch in a program to hear the tracks in the order you want them.

Easy operation and versatile manipulation of the laser disc are common to all compact disc players, sometimes called laser turntables.

Strong nerves and muscles

Optical guidance systems and electronics are more sophisticated. The lasers that read digital information off the disc and keep the beam on track, and the microprocessors that change light to sound, are cheaper to produce, lighter in weight and more reliable. Large-scale integrated circuits have replaced entire boards of electronic components. Tiny servos now guide the arm that carries the laser and do it more accurately than the massive linkages that were used originally.

Amazing memories

The latest digital logic circuitry can track the tiny micro-pits engraved on the spinning CD with exceptional single-mindedness. When dirt or scratches cause brief information dropouts, the decoding circuitry pulls replacement information from computer memories to patch these chuck-holes before the audio circuits of the player get the shock or dead spots of silence. There is so much compensating circuitry that audible glitches are rare, except when playing damaged or unusually faulty discs.

Speed readers

Readout panels show you how much time has elapsed or remains on a whole disc or just one track. All the information is on the discs, just waiting to be read. There are even four ways of repeating music: You can replay a whole disc, just one song, selections in the programmable memory or all music between two programmed points (A-B repeat). One final control feature is for the do-it-yourselfer who wants to locate music manually, as opposed to programming it in. This is music search, which samples brief bits of music as the laser skims over the disc.

Component systems

Some manufacturers design entire interrelated component systems, including CDs. Record synchronization lets you start a CD player and a cassette deck (set to record) with the touch of one button. Both stop at the same time. What about the possibility of future audio *and* video information packed onto CDs? Small as they are, compact discs have room enough for more than just the 70 minutes of stereo sound they currently can hold, and manufacturers have been searching for a technical standard for video images on CDs.

Equalizers for your stereo system

■ AN EQUALIZER GIVES YOU AMAZING control over the "shape" of your music. Just as your home listening room has its minor acoustic imperfections, recording engineers and record producers don't always deliver quite the sound mixture you may want. Tone controls—the knobs on your receiver that control bass and treble—are a fine feature, but nothing approaches the convenience and flexibility of an equalizer to iron out hot spots and fill in holes in the sound.

The bass tone control boosts all sound frequencies from the mid-range down; treble from the mid-range up. An equalizer lets you establish accurate control of all the frequencies to fit your equipment, your recordings, your taste and your listening environment. A 10-band equalizer (10 controls per stereo channel) is often called an *octave* equalizer. Each slide control adjusts one octave of sound frequencies. On simpler 5-band units, each control adjusts two octaves.

An equalizer does not create sounds that do not already exist. Most of the frequencies that you need to hear in your music are already recorded. Certain frequencies are simply not reproduced with as much volume as are the mid-range frequencies, which stretch from about 800Hz to 2000Hz.

The high frequencies determine the clarity and brilliance of your music. With an equalizer, you can bring cymbals to life at 16,000Hz, while at the same time you can cut tape hiss or annoying record scratches at 8000Hz. You can boost the low bass from 31.5Hz to 125Hz to animate specific areas or instruments. In the mid-range, you can boost trumpets at 300Hz to 500Hz or the clarinets at 100Hz.

No recording engineer or record maker can even begin to control your listening preferences or listening environment. Many people, as they grow older, require sounds at the higher frequencies to be louder to be heard at the same perceived level as sounds at lower frequencies. Furniture and wall coverings in your listening room can absorb some of the higher frequencies before you have a chance to hear them, or bounce the low frequencies back at you at louder levels than you would like. An equalizer on your stereo equipment will let you adjust the level of each musical octave to restore the clarity and brilliance of the higher frequencies and the presence created by the lower frequencies.

Most equalizers are *graphic* equalizers. When you set the sliders, their position forms a visual graph on the display screen. In some models, this display can also be used to analyze your stereo listening room. Each of the displays becomes a VU meter tuned to a specific octave of the sound spectrum. Using a microphone where you normally sit to listen, you adjust each corresponding control to increase or decrease any frequency range that is being distorted in your room.

It's not hard to learn how to match frequencies you hear to the frequencies indicated on the face of the equalizer. Many manufacturers include diagrams with their units showing the frequency range of various instruments and of our standard human voices: soprano, alto, tenor and bass. These charts give you a ready reference to use with your equalizer. In no time at all, you'll reach for the 1kHz slider when you need to adjust the upper mid-range. To de-emphasize a bass boom slightly, you'll instinctively drop the slider at 63Hz down a notch or two.

Just about all equalizers have a few things in common. Most feature controls to equalize music playing over the speakers, or to equalize material as you record it onto tape, or to perform both functions simultaneously. There's nearly always

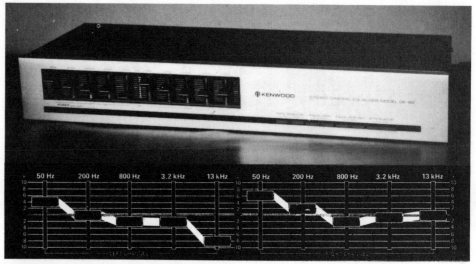

WHEN YOU MAKE TAPES FOR THE ROAD, pit an equalizer against your car's hostile acoustics. An equalizer such as the one shown can be used to iron out dead or boomy notes and restore realistic sound. This model features five bands in each stereo channel. Set as shown, it will damp high treble and coax more bass into the cassette you're recording for on-the-road enjoyment. Note that settings are a bit different on each channel to allow for such things as door-panel resonances.

THIS EQUALIZER is shown as you might adjust it to compensate for room furniture that swallows bass and highs but emphasizes the middle range of the music. The slider controls are set to apply a mid-bass boost, some mid-range reduction and substantial treble strengthening. The settings are actually exaggerated for illustration purposes in this photo, giving more boost and reduction than normally needed.

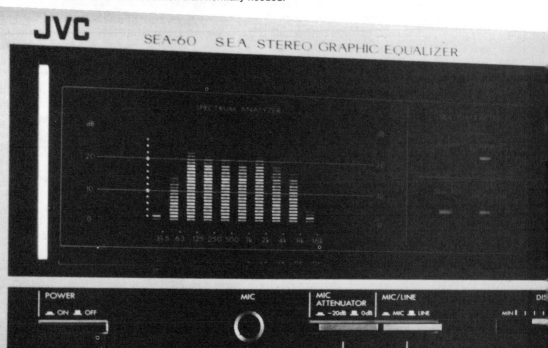

ANOTHER OPTION LETS YOU CORRECT loudspeakers to your taste, using subtle hints from an equalizer. The equalizer permits separate tuning for each stereo channel. In the model shown, it is used to cut extreme highs, boost deepest bass and supply reinforcement to the upper mid-range. If equalizer settings are more extreme, try repositioning the speakers in your room.

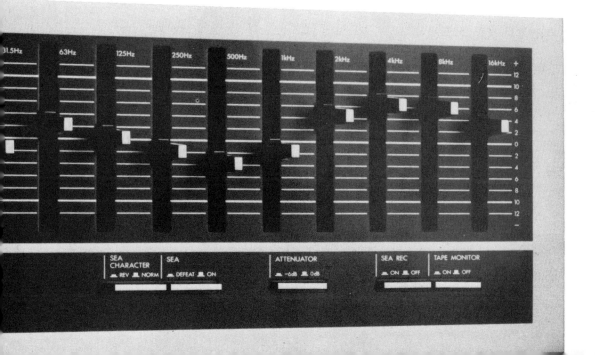

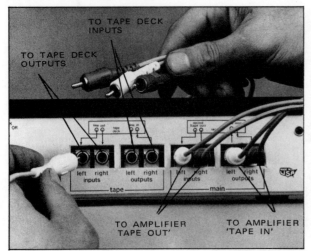

TO TAPE DECK
INPUTS

TO TAPE DECK
OUTPUTS

TO AMPLIFIER
'TAPE OUT'

TO AMPLIFIER
'TAPE IN'

TO HOOK UP AN EQUALIZER, connect patch cords into the tape-monitor loop of your amplifier. Left- and right-channel equalizer inputs go to the respective tape outputs on the back of the amplifier. The equalizer outputs also go to the amplifier, but to the tape inputs. To hear the equalization, switch on the amplifier's monitor circuit. You can also attach a tape deck as shown: the equalizer's outputs go to the deck's inputs; the equalizer's inputs to the deck's outputs.

a center line (labeled "O" or "Odb"), with pluses above and minuses below.

All equalizer models can alter the frequency spectrum as it goes onto tape. Most units do this simply by rerouting the appropriate signals at the touch of a control. A few require rearrangement of the rear-panel patch cords to do this.

Your ear is the most sensitive sound equipment you own. In many situations you can use an equalizer to contour musical sounds to suit your personal tastes. Before you confront an array of equalizers in the store, have a good idea of what you want an equalizer to do for you. You may want to tailor a wide variety of recordings to the sound you want, or you may wish to "fix" a car or listening room that has acoustic troubles. Or you may just want to bring back your younger days when you hear all frequencies with the same ease.

SHOP GUIDE

CUSTOMARY TO METRIC (CONVERSION) Conversion factors can be carried so far they become impractical. In cases below where an entry is exact it is followed by an asterisk (*). Where considerable rounding off has taken place, the entry is followed by a + or a − sign.

Linear Measure

inches	millimeters
1/16	1.5875*
1/8	3.2
3/16	4.8
1/4	6.35*
5/16	7.9
3/8	9.5
7/16	11.1
1/2	12.7*
9/16	14.3
5/8	15.9
11/16	17.5
3/4	19.05*
13/16	20.6
7/8	22.2
15/16	23.8
1	25.4*

inches	centimeters
1	2.54*
2	5.1
3	7.6
4	10.2
5	12.7*
6	15.2
7	17.8
8	20.3
9	22.9
10	25.4*
11	27.9
12	30.5

feet	centimeters	meters
1	30.48*	.3048*
2	61	.61
3	91	.91
4	122	1.22
5	152	1.52
6	183	1.83
7	213	2.13
8	244	2.44
9	274	2.74
10	305	3.05
50	1524*	15.24*
100	3048*	30.48*

1 yard = .9144* meters
1 rod = 5.0292* meters
1 mile = 1.6 kilometers
1 nautical mile = 1.852* kilometers

Weights

ounces	grams
1	28.3
2	56.7
3	85
4	113
5	142
6	170
7	198
8	227
9	255
10	283
11	312
12	340
13	369
14	397
15	425
16	454

Formula (exact):
ounces × 28.349 523 125* = grams

pounds	kilograms
1	.45
2	.9
3	1.4
4	1.8
5	2.3
6	2.7
7	3.2
8	3.6
9	4.1
10	4.5

1 short ton (2000 lbs) = 907 kilograms (kg)
Formula (exact):
pounds × .453 592 37* = kilograms

Fluid Measure

(Milliliters [ml] and cubic centimeters [cc] are equivalent, but it is customary to use milliliters for liquids.)

1 cu in	=	16.39 ml
1 fl oz	=	29.6 ml
1 cup	=	237 ml
1 pint	=	473 ml
1 quart	=	946 ml
	=	.946 liters
1 gallon	=	3785 ml
	=	3.785 liters

Formula (exact):
fluid ounces × 29.573 529 562 5* = milliliters

Volume

1 cu in	=	16.39 cubic centimeters (cc)
1 cu ft	=	28 316.7 cc
1 bushel	=	35 239.1 cc
1 peck	=	8 809.8 cc

Area

1 sq in	=	6.45 sq cm
1 sq ft	=	929 sq cm
	=	.093 sq meters
1 sq yd	=	.84 sq meters
1 acre	=	4 046.9 sq meters
	=	.404 7 hectares
1 sq mile	=	2 589 988 sq meters
	=	259 hectares
	=	2.589 9 sq kilometers

Miscellaneous

1 British thermal unit (Btu) (mean) = 1 055.9 joules
1 horsepower = 745.7 watts
= .75 kilowatts
caliber (diameter of a firearm's bore in hundredths of an inch) = .254 millimeters (mm)

1 atmosphere pressure = 101 325* pascals (newtons per sq meter)
1 pound per square inch (psi) = 6 895 pascals
1 pound per square foot = 47.9 pascals
1 knot = 1.85 kilometers per hour
1 mile per hour = 1.6093 kilometers per hour